SEARCH & FIND®
at the
Ferris Wheel
BEGINNERS
Alien
Hammock
Telephone
Helipcoter
guitarist
Bird house
Jumping duck
Sombrero
Flowerpot
Popcorn
Clock
Backhoe tractor
Arrow
Artist
Astronaut
Broom
Camera
Candy cane
Chimney
Crocodile
Giraffe
Golfer
Hockey stick
Ice skates
Kite
Lions (2)
Oilcan
"Oup and Doup"
Plumber's plunger
Santa Claus
Screw
Shovel
Surfer
Ticket collector
Umbrella
Volcano
Watering can
Answers on the back.
HELP!
SQUEAK!
I'M A STATUE!
WHAT DOES "SQUEAK" MEAN?
I MUST STOP SMOKING!
PAPA BEAR WANTS OUT!!
Z-Z-Z-Z!
SPLASH!
HI MOM!
I WANT TO GO HOME!
I'M GETTING ANGRY.
I'M JACK, THE COPY-CAT!!
CHIRP!
DO YOU SEE SUSIE?
IS SHE HERE?
I WANT OUT!
COMING SOON... A HOLE IN THE GROUND!
GREAT SHOT!
POP!
POP CORN
BOING!
HO!
WHAT DOES THAT SAY?
I'VE LANDED ON THE WRONG PLANET!
R-R-RING!
CONDEMNED
A-ONE... AND A TWO...
PEACE AND QUIET!
I'M LATE, I'M LATE.
IT'S MUCH BETTER THIS WAY!
HARE I AM!
WOW!
I'M HUNGRY!!
I MUST GO ON A DIET!
OOPS!
THIS IS FUN, OUP!
THIS REMINDS ME OF MY INVENTION, THE WHEEL, DOUP.
THIS IS NOT FOR ME!
WHO?
KER-PLUNK!
EAT AT DINO'S
IT MIGHT RAIN.
NEVER AGAIN!
THIS LOOKS LIKE FUN!!
COME ON, PAPA BEAR!
NO WAY!
WHO IS NEXT?
MY KIND OF RIDE!
SPLAT!
QUICK SAND!

ANSWERS

SQUEAK!
SPLASH!
HI MOM!
HELP!
I'M A STATUE!
I MUST STOP SMOKING!
PAPA BEAR WANTS OUT!!
WHAT DOES "SQUEAK" MEAN?
GREAT SHOT!
COMING SOON... A HOLE IN THE GROUND!
BOING!
I WANT TO GO HOME!
CHIRP!
I WANT OUT!
I'M JACK, THE COPY-CAT!!
DO YOU SEE SUSIE?
IS SHE HERE?
WHAT DOES THAT SAY?
CONDEMNED
POP!
POP-CORN
HO!
I'VE LANDED ON THE WRONG PLANET!
PEACE AND QUIET!
IT'S MUCH BETTER THIS WAY!
WET PAINT
HARE I AM!
WOW!
I MUST GO ON A DIET!
I'M HUNGRY!!
OOPS!
THIS IS FUN, OUP!
THIS REMINDS ME OF MY INVENTION, THE WHEEL, OOUP.
EAT AT DINO'S
THIS IS NOT FOR ME.
WHO?
IT MIGHT RAIN.
NEVER AGAIN!
THIS LOOKS LIKE FUN!!
COME ON, PAPA BEAR!
NO WAY!
WHO IS NEXT?
SPLAT!
QUICK SAND!
MY KIND OF RIDE!

SEARCH & FIND®
at the Dog School

- "Barking King I" sign
- Briefcases (3)
- Canes (2)
- Cat litter
- Clipboard
- Crown
- Crying dog
- "Dog Days"
- "Doggy Decimal System"
- "Dog Tail"
- Empty dog bowls (14)
- Fire hydrant
- Graduate's hat
- Hammer
- Ladle
- Man on leash
- Napkins (2)
- Pearl necklace
- Roller skates
- Ruler
- Screwdriver
- Sleeping dog
- Spoons (3)
- Stool
- Straw
- Sunglasses

Answers on the back.

ANSWERS

A ARF
B BOW
C CAR
DOG
DOG SCHOOL
NAME THIS!
DOG DAYS
PSSST! DO YOU WANT TO CHASE A CAR?
LIBRARY NO BARKING ZONE
DOG TALES
HISTORY OF BONES
DOG TAIL
I INVENTED THE DOGGY BANK!
DOG-WOOD
DOGGY DECIMAL SYSTEM
HOLD STILL.
SERVANT!
SLAVE!
MAN!
MASTER!
GOPHER!
I BROUGHT HIM FOR SHOW AND TELL.
P.T.A. POOCH TRAINERS ASSOCIATION
LET IT BE SUMMER VACATION TIME!
THIS IS MY SCIENCE PROJECT... FRANKENDOG!
ER...
STOP THAT!
PLEASE DO MY HOMEWORK!
BARKING 1
HIGHER!
BARKING KING I
QUIET SERIOUS STUDY IN PROGRESS
ARF!
ARF, ARF!
ARF, ARF, ARF!
ARF, ARF, ARF, ARF!
TAKE ALL YOU WANT. EAT ALL YOU TAKE!
CHOW TIME. YUM!
BONES
MUSH
STEAK
SHOW US WHAT YOU'VE LEARNED.
HOW TO BARK
TAIL WAG!
SIT!
BARK!
BEG!
CRY!
JUVENILES!
ROLL OVER!
VANISH!
FETCH!
HOWL!
LOOKS GOOD.
FINISHED!
DULL!
GOAL!
TRICK!
HI MOM!
STAY!
ATTACK!
TOE!
OBEDIENCE CLASS
SHOP CLASS
WE MUST HAVE DONE SOMETHING WRONG!
HOW TO BUILD A DOGHOUSE
DOGGY BAG
SUPER DOG

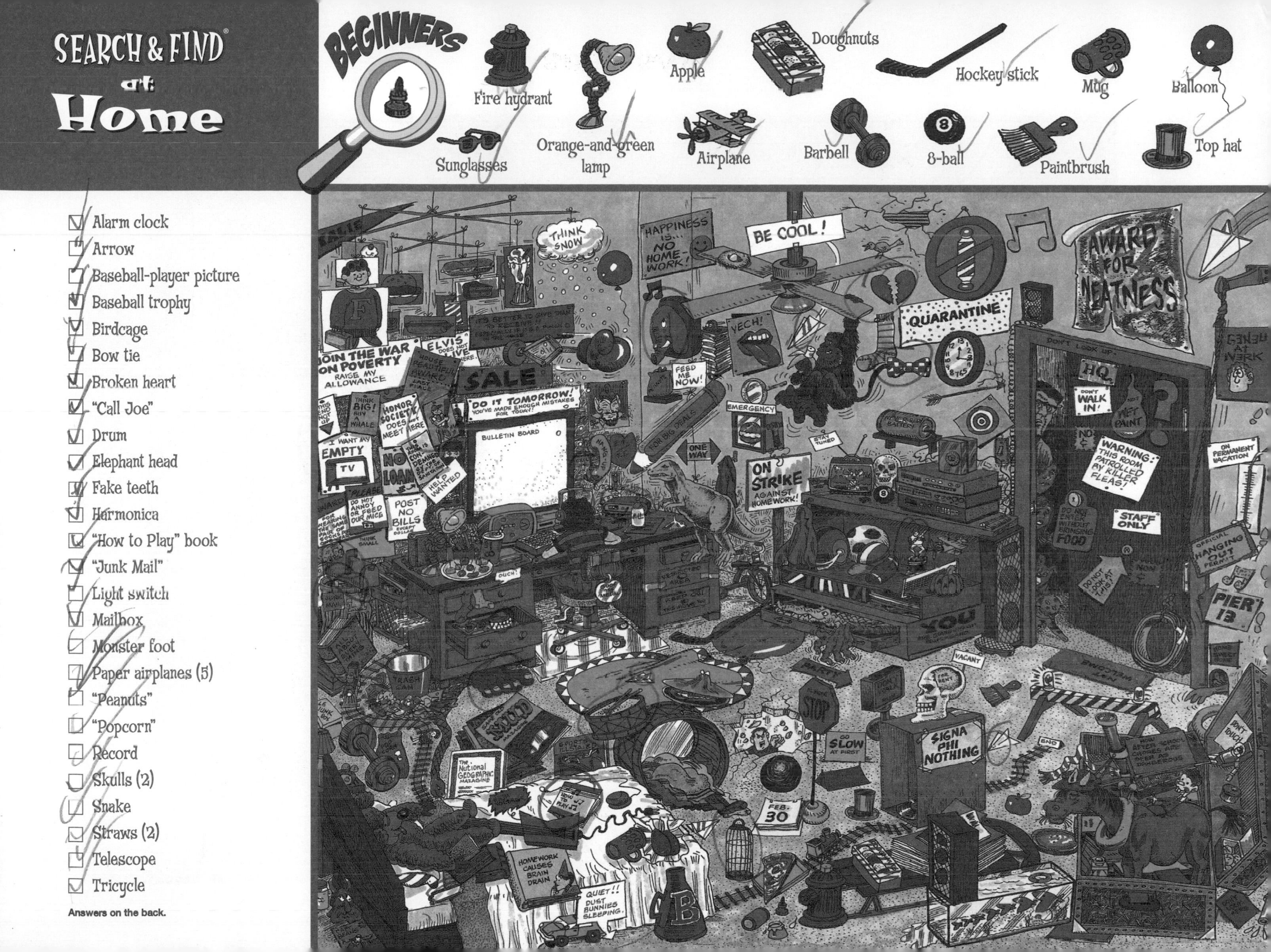

SEARCH & FIND®
at
Home
BEGINNERS
Fire hydrant
Apple
Doughnuts
Hockey stick
Mug
Balloon
Sunglasses
Orange-and-green lamp
Airplane
Barbell
8-ball
Paintbrush
Top hat
Alarm clock
Arrow
Baseball-player picture
Baseball trophy
Birdcage
Bow tie
Broken heart
"Call Joe"
Drum
Elephant head
Fake teeth
Harmonica
"How to Play" book
"Junk Mail"
Light switch
Mailbox
Monster foot
Paper airplanes (5)
"Peanuts"
"Popcorn"
Record
Skulls (2)
Snake
Straws (2)
Telescope
Tricycle
Answers on the back.
THINK SNOW
HAPPINESS IS... NO HOME-WORK!
BE COOL!
AWARD FOR NEATNESS
QUARANTINE
JOIN THE WAR ON POVERTY RAISE MY ALLOWANCE
SALE
DO IT TOMORROW! YOU'VE MADE ENOUGH MISTAKES FOR TODAY!
BULLETIN BOARD
YECH!
FEED ME NOW!
EMERGENCY
ONE WAY
ON STRIKE AGAINST HOMEWORK!
STAY TUNED
HQ
DON'T WALK IN!
WET PAINT
WARNING: THIS ROOM PATROLLED BY KILLER FLEAS!
STAFF ONLY
ON PERMANENT VACATION
OFFICIAL HANGING OUT PERMIT
PIER 13
I WANT MY EMPTY TV
POST NO BILLS
HELP WANTED
NO LOAN
HONOR SOCIETY DOES NOT MEET HERE
DO NOT ANNOY OR FEED OUR MICE
YOU
VACANT
STOP
SLOW
SIGNA PHI NOTHING
FEB. 30
The National GEOGRAPHIC MAGAZINE
HOMEWORK CAUSES BRAIN DRAIN
QUIET!! DUST BUNNIES SLEEPING.
TRASH CAN
OUCH!
END

ANSWERS

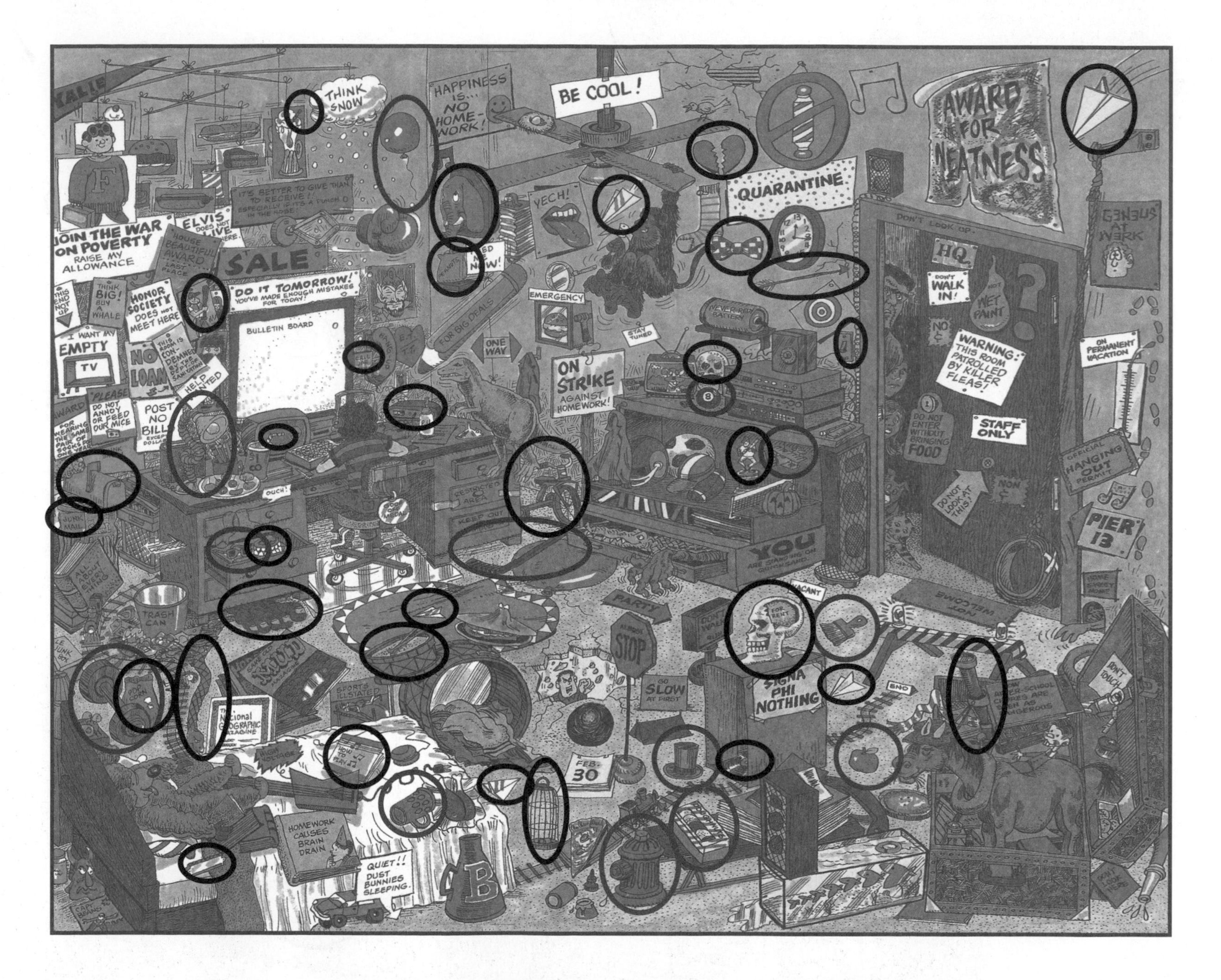

THINK SNOW
HAPPINESS IS... NO HOME-WORK!
BE COOL!
AWARD FOR NEATNESS
IT'S BETTER TO GIVE THAN TO RECEIVE! ESPECIALLY IF IT'S A PUNCH IN THE NOSE.
YECH!
QUARANTINE
JOIN THE WAR ON POVERTY
RAISE MY ALLOWANCE
ELVIS DOES NOT LIVE HERE
HOUSE BEAUTIFUL AWARD
SALE
DO IT TOMORROW! YOU'VE MADE ENOUGH MISTAKES FOR TODAY!
THINK BIG! BUY A WHALE
HONOR SOCIETY DOES NOT MEET HERE
BULLETIN BOARD
FOR BIG DEALS
EMERGENCY
ONE WAY
STAY TUNED
NEVER-REST BATTERY
DON'T LOOK UP.
HQ
DON'T WALK IN!
NOT WET PAINT
WARNING: THIS ROOM PATROLLED BY KILLER FLEAS!
GENEUS AT WERK
ON PERMANENT VACATION
I WANT MY EMPTY TV
NO LOAN
THIS ROOM IS CONDEMNED
HELP WANTED
ON STRIKE AGAINST HOMEWORK!
*PLEASE DO NOT ANNOY OR FEED OUR MICE
POST NO BILLS
DO NOT ENTER WITHOUT BRINGING FOOD
STAFF ONLY
OFFICIAL HANGING OUT PERMIT
DO NOT LOOK AT THIS!
PIER 13
OUCH!
RESTRICTED AREA
KEEP OUT
YOU ARE STANDING ON QUICKSAND
NOT WELCOME
TRASH CAN
PARTY
VACANT
FOR RENT
STOP
GO SLOW AT FIRST
SIGMA PHI NOTHING
SPORTS ILLUSTRATED
The National Geographic Magazine
FEB. 30
HOMEWORK CAUSES BRAIN DRAIN
QUIET!! DUST BUNNIES SLEEPING.
DON'T TOUCH
B

SEARCH & FIND®

After School

- [ ] Balloon
- [ ] Basketballs (2)
- [ ] Baton
- [ ] Beard
- [ ] Bird
- [ ] Bus Driver
- [ ] Chimney
- [ ] Clock faces (2)
- [ ] Donkey
- [ ] Fish wearing a hat
- [ ] Grocery cart
- [ ] Hat with propeller
- [ ] Huck Finn
- [ ] Igloo
- [ ] Mice (3)
- [ ] Paper hat
- [ ] Parrot
- [ ] Pencil
- [ ] Pig
- [ ] Radio
- [ ] Robot
- [ ] Smelly potion
- [ ] Snowman
- [ ] Stool
- [ ] Sunglasses
- [ ] Unicorn

Answers on the back.

ANSWERS

IS SCHOOL OVER SO SOON?
SCHOOL BUILDING CONDEMNED
MY SHIP IS LEAVING WITHOUT ME!
FEET DO YOUR THING!
WHERE'S THE ICE?
I JUST KICKED THE BUCKET!
AND AWAY I GO!!
STUDENTS NOT WORKING
WAKE ME WHEN IT'S OVER.
TAKE THE PICTURE!
I'M THE SCHOOL SPIRIT.
I'M THE SCHOOL MASCOT!
YOU'RE THE SCHOOL BRAIN-DRAIN!
HOW IS THIS?
UGH!
HELLO, VICTOR!
HOORAY! I DID IT!
I'M OVER HERE, JUNIOR! IT'S MOMMY!
I'M LOST!
HE REALLY DID IT!
BUT IT WAS A SUNDAY WHEN HE DID IT!?
IT'S FROM MY SCIENCE CLASS.
DO NOT READ THIS.
IS HE GOING TO STEP ON THAT MOUSE?
NO. I THINK IT'LL SQUEAK BY.
YOU'LL GET A SEAT ON THE BUS FOR SURE!
DO I LOOK COOL?
NOT NEXT TO ME!
IT'S MY MOMMY!
HELP!
I'LL TACKLE HIM NOW!
ONCE A MONTH WHETHER YOU NEED TO OR NOT.
I DIDN'T KNOW YOU COULD TELL TIME!
THE GAME ENDED YESTERDAY!
WE LOST!
-DANGER- LIVE STUDENTS INSIDE
THIS WAY TO THE SCHOOL BUS.
YES, SIR!
YOU WILL SIT QUIETLY IN MY BUS!
I BURNED THE MILK SHAKE IN MY COOKING CLASS!
I GRADUATED FROM SCHOOL.
HI!
CAN YOU CARRY MY BOOK?
I FLUNKED LUNCH.
I LIKE IT SO MUCH THAT I'M TAKING IT HOME!
TRASH

SEARCH & FIND® at the Dog Mall

- Air conditioner
- "Bone on a Bun"
- Bookstore
- Cats (2)
- Chef's hat
- Cookies (2)
- Crooked chimney
- Fire hydrants (2)
- Flamingo
- Food court
- "For Rent"
- Graduate
- Headphones
- Hockey stick
- "Hunk" poster
- K-9 Mart
- Leashes (3)
- Lollipop
- Mug
- Scissors
- Shoe
- Spotlight
- Stool
- Suitcase
- Sunglasses
- Tennis racket

Answers on the back.

ANSWERS

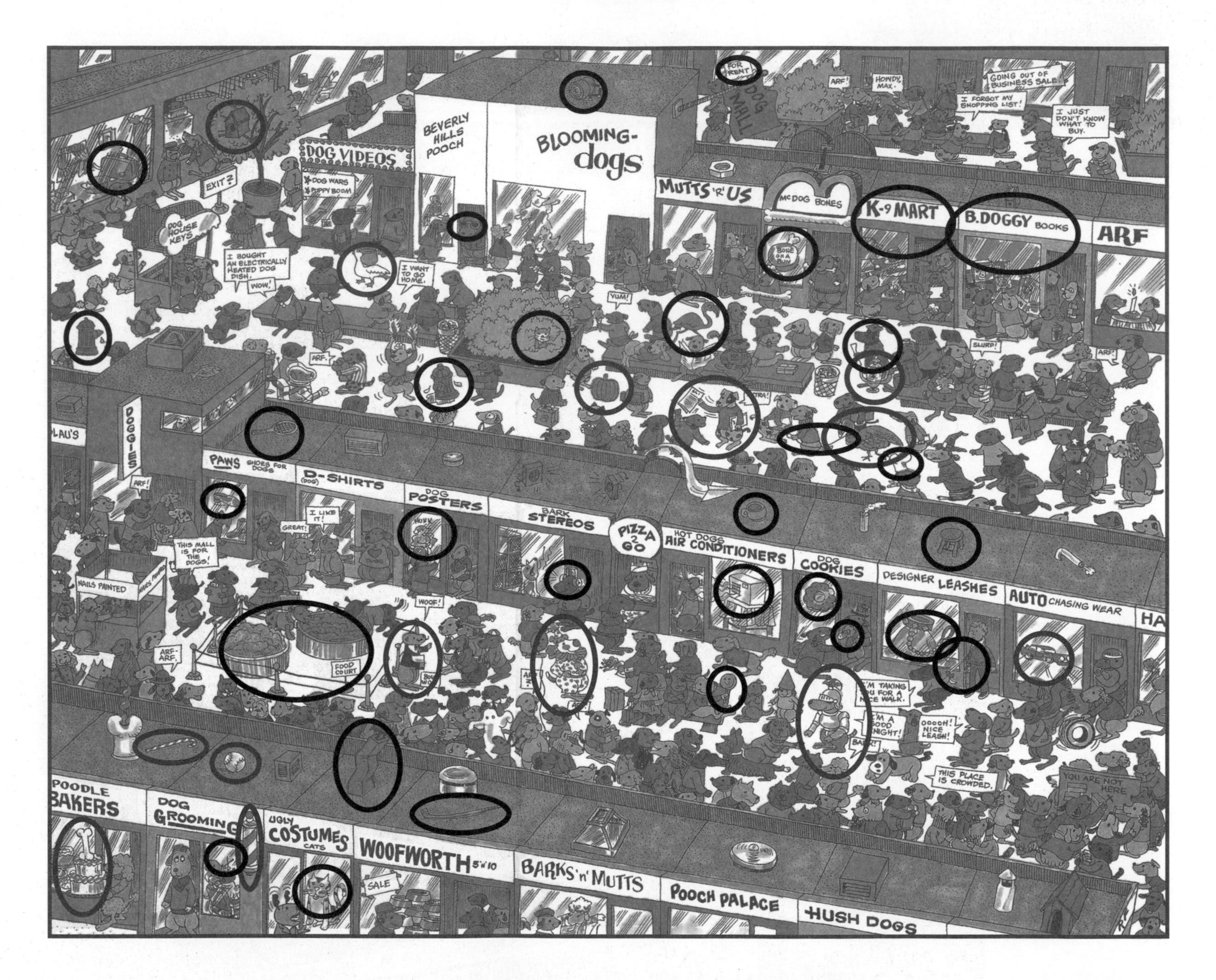

FOR RENT
DOG MALL
ARF!
HOWDY, MAX.
GOING OUT OF BUSINESS SALE
I FORGOT MY SHOPPING LIST!
I JUST DON'T KNOW WHAT TO BUY.
BEVERLY HILLS POOCH
BLOOMING-dogs
DOG VIDEOS
DOG WARS
PUPPY BOOM
EXIT
DOG HOUSE KEYS
I BOUGHT AN ELECTRICALLY HEATED DOG DISH.
WOW!
I WANT TO GO HOME.
MUTTS 'R' US
McDOG BONES
K-9 MART
B. DOGGY BOOKS
ARF
YUM!
SLURP!
ARF.
DOGGIES
PAWS SHOES FOR DOGS
D-SHIRTS (DOG)
DOG POSTERS
BARK STEREOS
PIZZA 2 GO
HOT DOGS
AIR CONDITIONERS
DOG COOKIES
DESIGNER LEASHES
AUTO CHASING WEAR
I LIKE IT!
GREAT!
THIS MALL IS FOR THE DOGS!
NAILS PAINTED
WOOF!
ARF-ARF.
FOOD COURT
I'M TAKING YOU FOR A NICE WALK.
I'M A GOOD KNIGHT!
OOOOH! NICE LEASH!
THIS PLACE IS CROWDED.
YOU ARE NOT HERE
POODLE BAKERS
DOG GROOMING
UGLY COSTUMES CATS
WOOFWORTH 5¢ 10
SALE
BARKS 'n' MUTTS
POOCH PALACE
HUSH DOGS

SEARCH & FIND® at the Airport

- ☐ Binoculars
- ☐ Birdcage
- ☐ Chair
- ☐ Clothesline
- ☐ Clothespins (6)
- ☐ Football
- ☐ Green checkered pants
- ☐ Guardhouse
- ☐ Hammock
- ☐ Harpoon
- ☐ Helicopters (2)
- ☐ Hot-air balloon
- ☐ Hot dogs (2)
- ☐ Ice-cream cones (2)
- ☐ Kite
- ☐ Lost wallet
- ☐ Manholes (2)
- ☐ Paint rollers (2)
- ☐ Paper airplanes (3)
- ☐ Parachute
- ☐ Pear
- ☐ "Pequod"
- ☐ Pizza
- ☐ Roller coaster
- ☐ Tepee
- ☐ Wind "sock"

Answers on the back.

ANSWERS

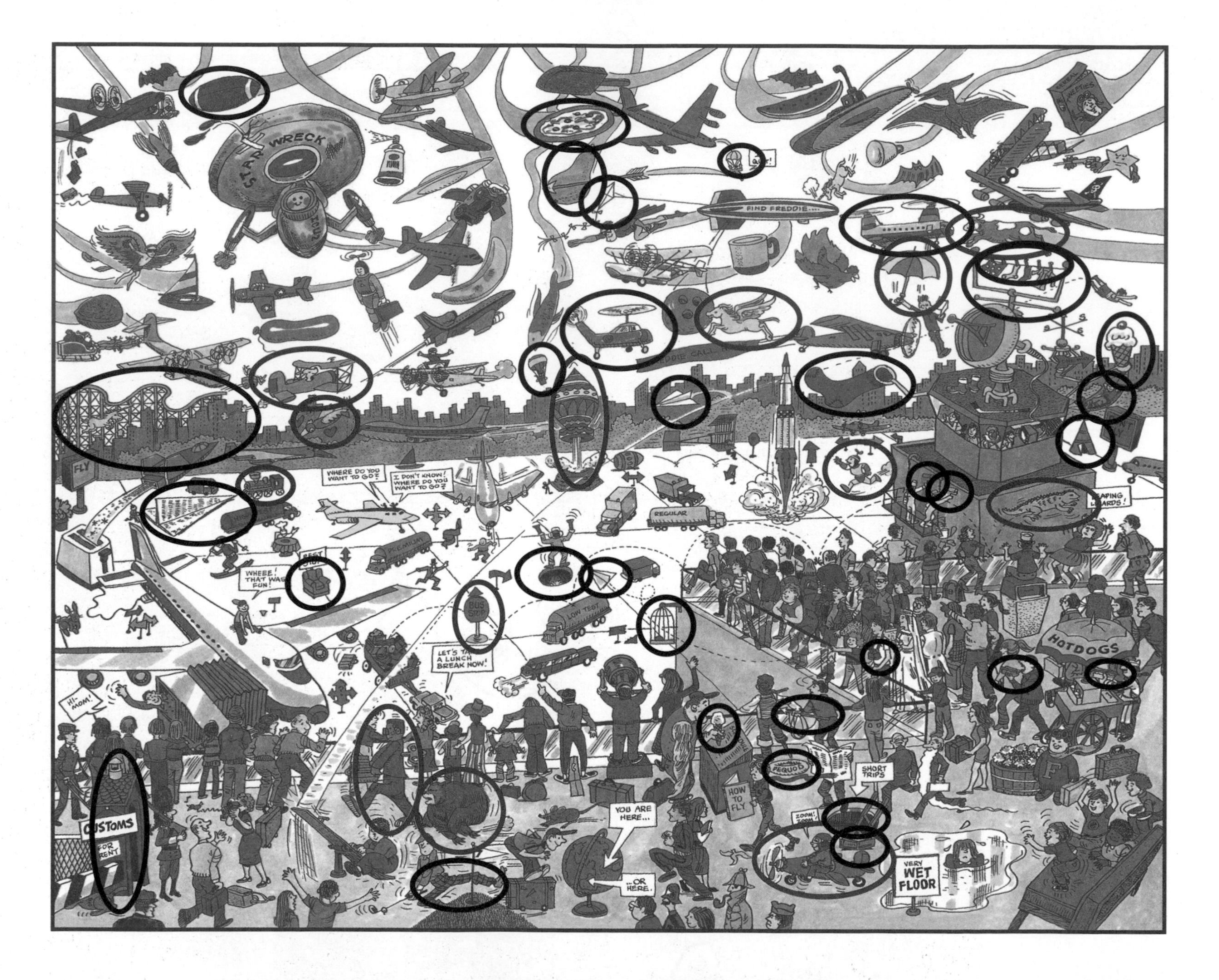
STAR WRECK
FIND FREDDIE...
FLY
WHERE DO YOU WANT TO GO?
I DON'T KNOW! WHERE DO YOU WANT TO GO?
REGULAR
PREMIUM
WHEEE! THAT WAS FUN!
BUS STOP
LOW TEST
A LUNCH BREAK NOW!
HI, MOM!
CUSTOMS
YOU ARE HERE...
...OR HERE.
HOW TO FLY
SHORT TRIPS
ZOOM! ZOOM!
VERY WET FLOOR
HOTDOGS

SEARCH & FIND®
at
School
BEGINNERS
Headstand
Jump rope
Mail carrier
Robot
Ship
Soccer ball
Bird
Tennis player
Kite
Jack-o'-lantern
Roller skater
Hamburger
Air pump
Barbells (2)
Baseballs (2)
Basketballs (3)
Bench
Briefcases (2)
Broken windows (2)
Butterfly net
Cake
Fish (2)
Fishing pole
Guitar
Horse
Magic carpet
Mouse
Mud puddle
Musical notes (2)
Paper airplanes (5)
Pillow
Rabbits (2)
Report Cards (5)
Skull
Swing set
Telescope
Trash can
Tug-of-war
Answers on the back.
BUILDING CONDEMNED
PASS THE HAMBURGER, PLEASE!
PLAY THIS? I CAN'T EVEN CARRY IT!
IF IT COULD ONLY TAKE MY EXAMS?
BAN DIRTY AIR
IT'S FOR SHOW AND TELL.
PLOP!
WHEN DO I GRADUATE?
WHEN BEAR MOUNTAIN HAS CUBS!
WHEN NIAGARA FALLS!
VOTE FREDDIE FOR SCHOOL PRESIDENT
ALMOST WET PAINT
SCHOOL CLOSED
REPORT CARD

ANSWERS

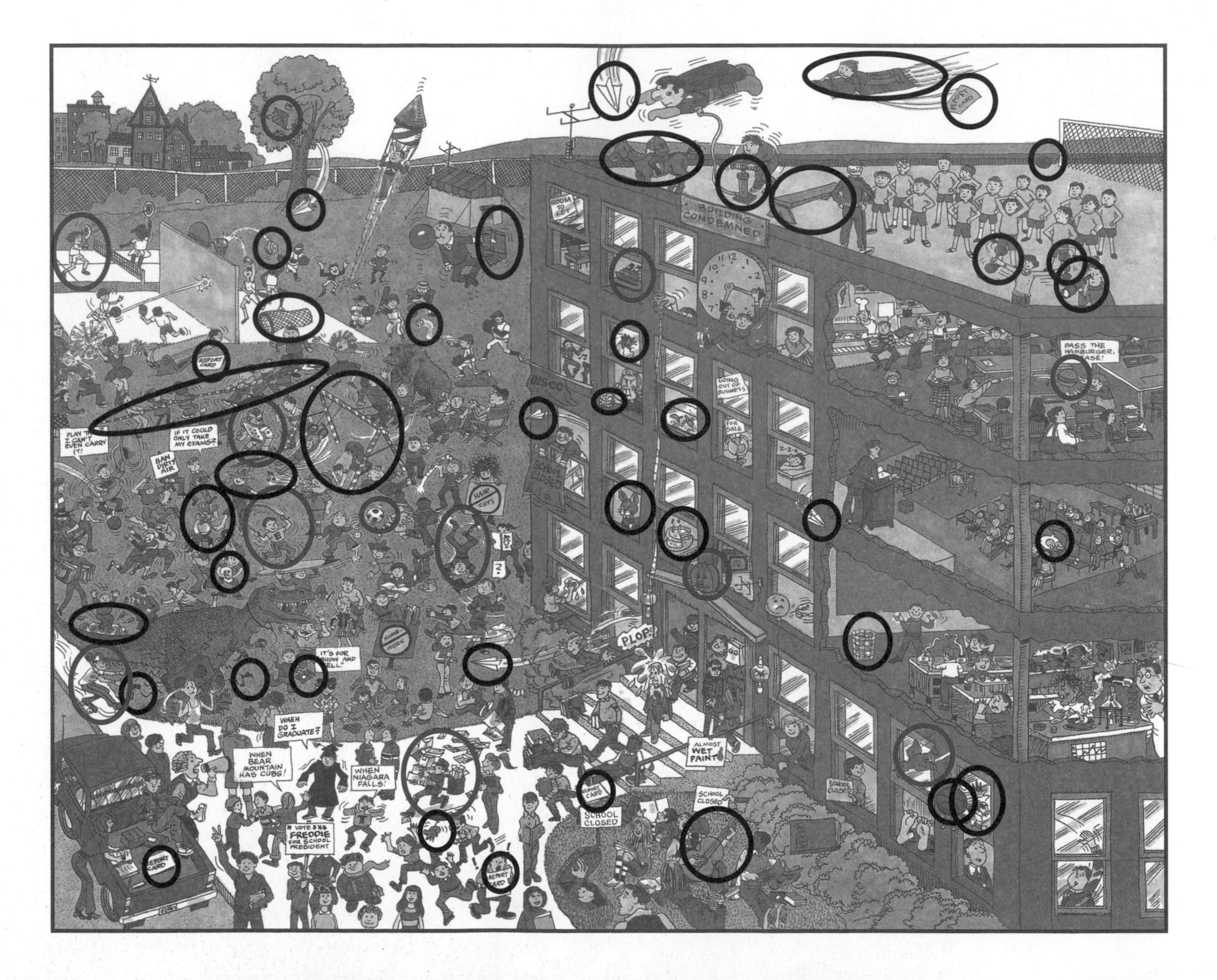

ROOM TO LET
BUILDING CONDEMNED
PASS THE HAMBURGER, PLEASE!
DISCO
GOING OUT OF BUSINESS
FOR SALE
SCHOOL CLOSED
REPORT CARD
PLAY IT? I CAN'T EVEN CARRY IT!
IF IT COULD ONLY TAKE MY EXAMS!
BAN DIRTY AIR
HAIR CUTS
HOME-WORK
IT'S FOR SHOW AND TELL.
PLOP!
ALMOST WET PAINT
WHEN DO I GRADUATE?
WHEN BEAR MOUNTAIN HAS CUBS!
WHEN NIAGARA FALLS!
VOTE FREDDIE FOR SCHOOL PRESIDENT
SCHOOL CLOSED

SEARCH & FIND® at the Ballpark

- ☐ Balloons (7)
- ☐ Banana
- ☐ Baseball bats (10)
- ☐ Basketball hoop
- ☐ Binoculars
- ☐ Blimp
- ☐ Carrot
- ☐ Clipboard
- ☐ Clothesline
- ☐ Cook
- ☐ Cowboy hat
- ☐ "Detour"
- ☐ Giraffe
- ☐ Horse
- ☐ Kite
- ☐ Ladder
- ☐ Lost shoe
- ☐ Money
- ☐ Mousehole
- ☐ "No. 1" hands (6)
- ☐ Periscope
- ☐ Pickax
- ☐ Police officers (2)
- ☐ Ripped pants
- ☐ Sunbather
- ☐ Sword

Answers on the back.

ANSWERS

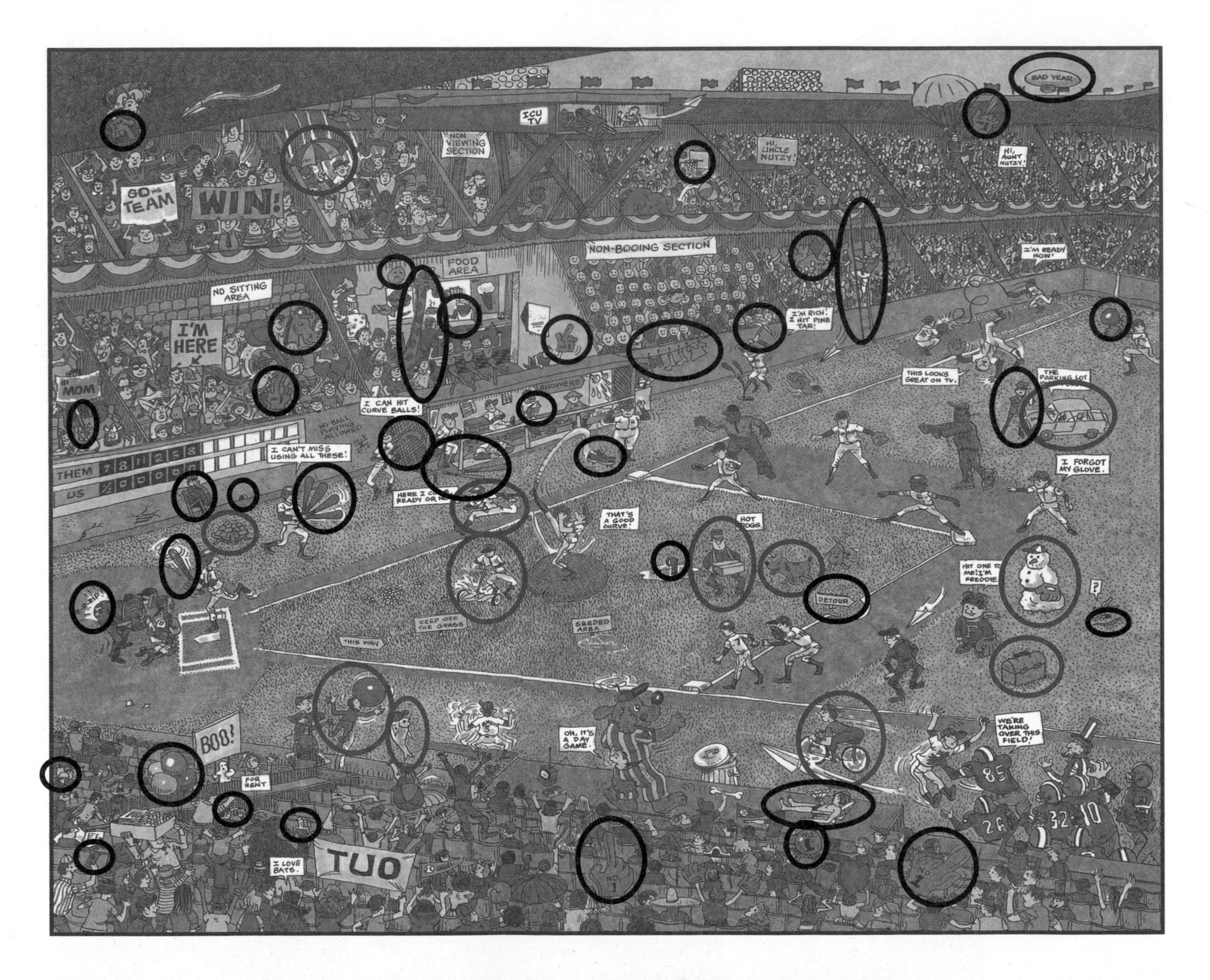
BAD YEAR
ICU TV
NON VIEWING SECTION
HI, UNCLE NUTZY!
HI, AUNT NUTZY!
GO TEAM
WIN!
NON-BOOING SECTION
FOOD AREA
NO SITTING AREA
I'M HERE
HI MOM
I'M READY NOW!
I'M RICH! I HIT PINE TAR!
THIS LOOKS GREAT ON TV.
I CAN HIT CURVE BALLS!
NO BALL PLAYING ALLOWED
SHOWERS
I CAN'T MISS USING ALL THESE!
THEM
US
I FORGOT MY GLOVE.
THAT'S A GOOD CURVE!
HOT DOGS
HIT ONE TO ME! I'M FREDDIE.
DETOUR
KEEP OFF THE GRASS
SEEDED AREA
THIS WAY
BOO!
FOR RENT
OH, IT'S A DAY GAME.
WE'RE TAKING OVER THIS FIELD!
I LOVE BATS.
TUO

SEARCH & FIND® at the Beach

- Barrel
- Clothespin
- Dog chasing cat
- Duck
- Eight ball
- Elephant
- Flamingo
- Flying car
- “Fresh Sand”
- Giant sandwich
- Golfers (2)
- Handstand surfer
- Helicopter
- Hot-air balloon
- Lighthouse
- Mice (2)
- Motorcycle
- Octopus
- Open umbrellas (6)
- “Quicksand”
- Rowboat
- Scuba diver
- Sheriff
- Shovel
- Tent
- Turtles (6)

Answers on the back.

ANSWERS

NOT FOR RENT
POST NO BILLS HERE
FOR RENT
FOR SALE
KEEP OFF
NO WAY
DON'T READ THIS
SEA SICK
I'M SITTING ON THIS ROCK.
FRESH FISH
I'M LOST!
WHICH WAY'S THE WATER?
I WANT A PEANUT BUTTER SANDWICH.
I HAVE A SAND SANDWICH!
WANT TO BUY A DUCK?
USED SAND
NEW SAND
QUICK-SAND
FOR RENT
JUNK DUMP
FRESH SAND
SAND SALE GOOD FOR CASTLES

SEARCH & FIND®
at the
Big Sale
BEGINNERS
Fish
Cartwheel man
Skier
Janitor
Long underwear
Fairy godmother
Mouse
Manhole
Robot
Pogo stick
Shopper
Turtle
Balloon
Cash register
Clothespins (9)
Count Dracula
Disappearing men (2)
"Don't Stop Shopping"
Fishing pole
Flower hat
Football
Football helmet
Gumball machine
Magic mirror
Octopus
Paint can
Paper airplane
Pig
Polka-dot shorts
Rabbit
Rocket
Roller skates
Santa Claus
Shirtless shopper
Ski jump
Skis (8)
Superhero
Telescope
Answers on the back.
SKI WEAR
THINK SNOW
WHERE IS THE TALL PERSON'S SHOP?
I NEED A SNACK.
I RAN OUT OF MONEY!
Z-Z-Z-Z-Z!
BOOKS
TOYS
SALE
STALE
THESE ARE ALL FOR THE LEFT FOOT.
I NEED A NEW CAPE!
SAVE
THIS IS THE SAFEST PLACE!
MY FAVORITE PERFUME, "UGY."
SMELLS GREAT!
THIS IS THE ONLY WAY TO SHOP.
OOPS!
I HOOKED ONE.
THIS WON'T FIT ME!
NOW I CAN GET TO THE COUNTER.
FALLING PRICE ZONE
THIS IS THE WAY TO SHOP.
WHERE ARE THE TOYS?
HO-HO-HO!
THIS IS MINE.
IS IT THE RIGHT SIZE?
AHHH! THAT FEELS GOOD.
WHERE IS THE FISH DEPARTMENT?
I CAN SHOP BETTER FROM UP HERE.
IT'S THE SHIRT OFF MY BACK!
I CAN'T REACH!
TO THE BETTER BLOUSE DEPARTMENT, JAMES.
YES, MADAM.
I'M LOST!
WHOOPS!!
HALF OFF!
1/2 OFF
IT'S THE LAST ONE!
I DON'T KNOW!
Z-Z-Z-Z!
WHAT IS IT?
WHERE ARE THE TOYS?
I JUST STARTED SHOPPING!
I SHOULD HAVE BEEN AT WORK YESTERDAY!
I LOOK GOOD IN THIS!
EXCELLENT!
HE'S "SPENT OUT!"
DO YOU LIKE THIS ON ME?
I THINK IT NEEDS WATER.
I WANT THAT!
THIS STORE IS NOT EVEN OPEN FOR BUSINESS YET!

ANSWERS

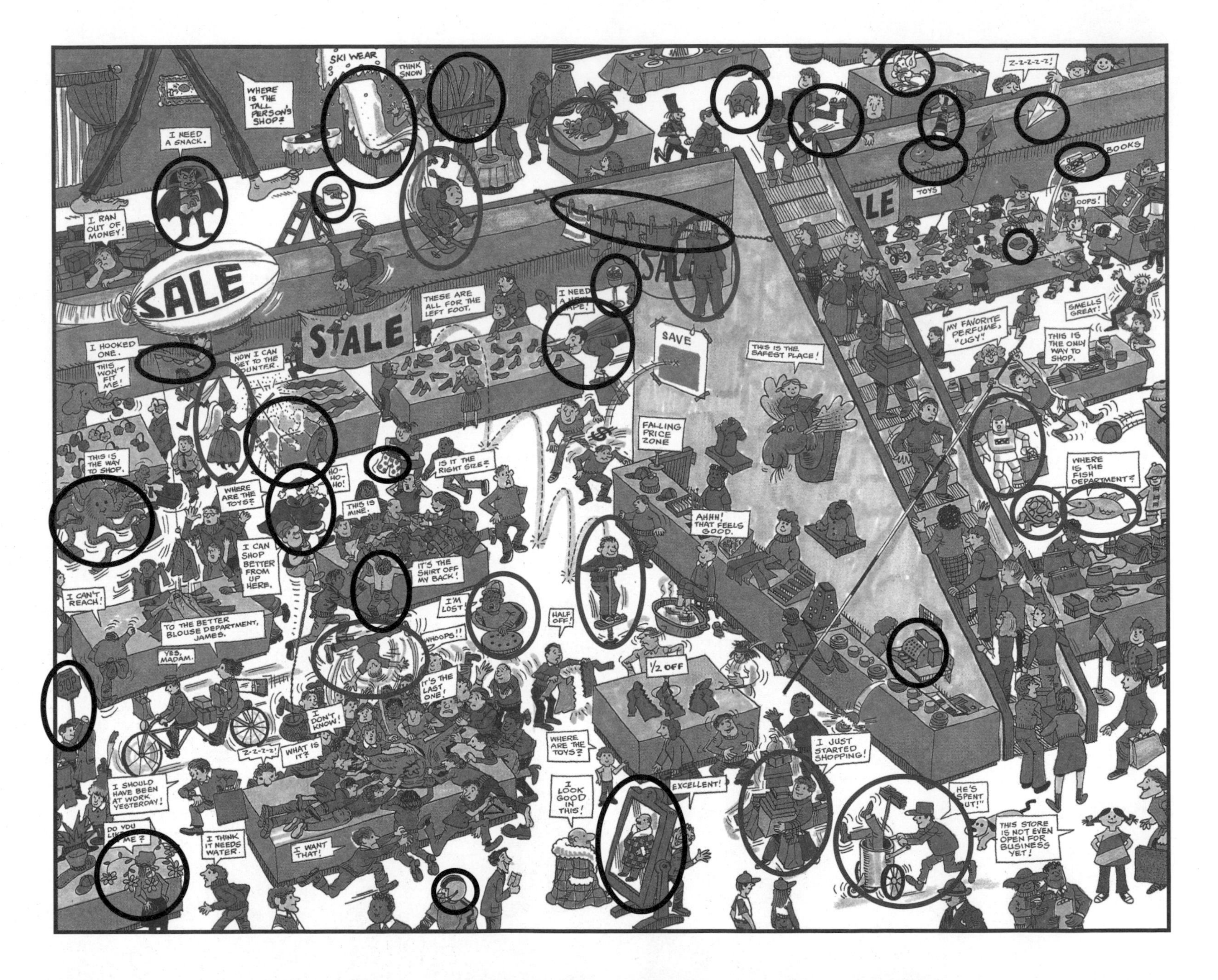

SKI WEAR
THINK SNOW
WHERE IS THE TALL PERSON'S SHOP?
I NEED A SNACK.
I RAN OUT OF MONEY!
SALE
STALE
THESE ARE ALL FOR THE LEFT FOOT.
Z-Z-Z-Z-Z!
BOOKS
TOYS
OOPS!
SMELLS GREAT!
MY FAVORITE PERFUME, "UGY."
THIS IS THE ONLY WAY TO SHOP.
I HOOKED ONE.
THIS WON'T FIT ME!
SAVE
THIS IS THE SAFEST PLACE!
FALLING PRICE ZONE
THIS IS THE WAY TO SHOP.
IS IT THE RIGHT SIZE?
WHERE ARE THE TOYS?
THIS IS MINE.
WHERE IS THE FISH DEPARTMENT?
AHHH! THAT FEELS GOOD.
I CAN SHOP BETTER FROM UP HERE.
IT'S THE SHIRT OFF MY BACK!
I'M LOST!
I CAN'T REACH!
TO THE BETTER BLOUSE DEPARTMENT, JAMES.
YES, MADAM.
HALF OFF!
WHOOPS!!
1/2 OFF
IT'S THE LAST ONE!
I DON'T KNOW!
STOP
Z-Z-Z-Z!
WHAT IS IT?
WHERE ARE THE TOYS?
I JUST STARTED SHOPPING!
I SHOULD HAVE BEEN AT WORK YESTERDAY!
I LOOK GOOD IN THIS!
EXCELLENT!
THIS STORE IS NOT EVEN OPEN FOR BUSINESS YET!
I THINK IT NEEDS WATER.
I WANT THAT!

SEARCH & FIND® on a Bus Trip

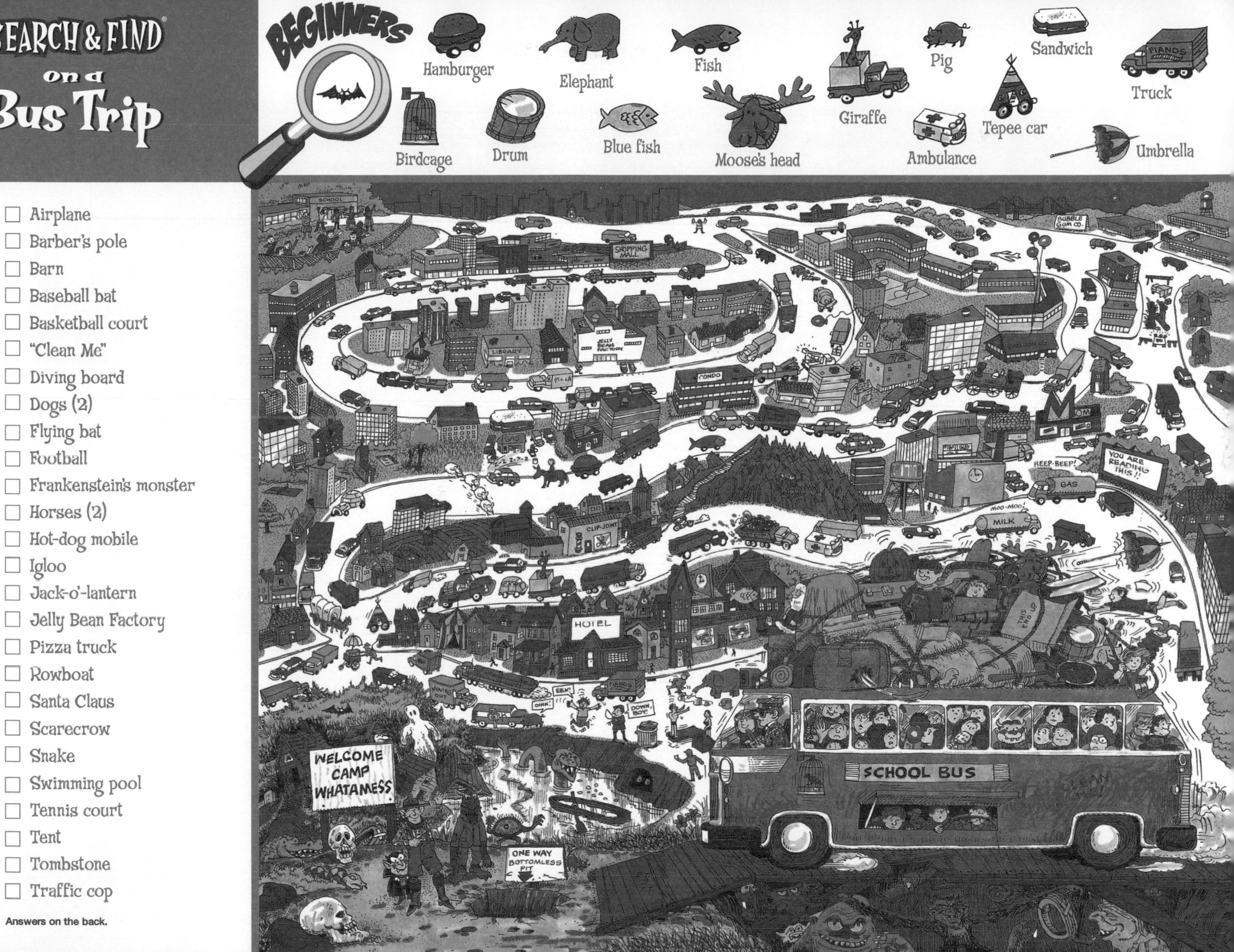

- ☐ Airplane
- ☐ Barber's pole
- ☐ Barn
- ☐ Baseball bat
- ☐ Basketball court
- ☐ "Clean Me"
- ☐ Diving board
- ☐ Dogs (2)
- ☐ Flying bat
- ☐ Football
- ☐ Frankenstein's monster
- ☐ Horses (2)
- ☐ Hot-dog mobile
- ☐ Igloo
- ☐ Jack-o'-lantern
- ☐ Jelly Bean Factory
- ☐ Pizza truck
- ☐ Rowboat
- ☐ Santa Claus
- ☐ Scarecrow
- ☐ Snake
- ☐ Swimming pool
- ☐ Tennis court
- ☐ Tent
- ☐ Tombstone
- ☐ Traffic cop

Answers on the back.

ANSWERS

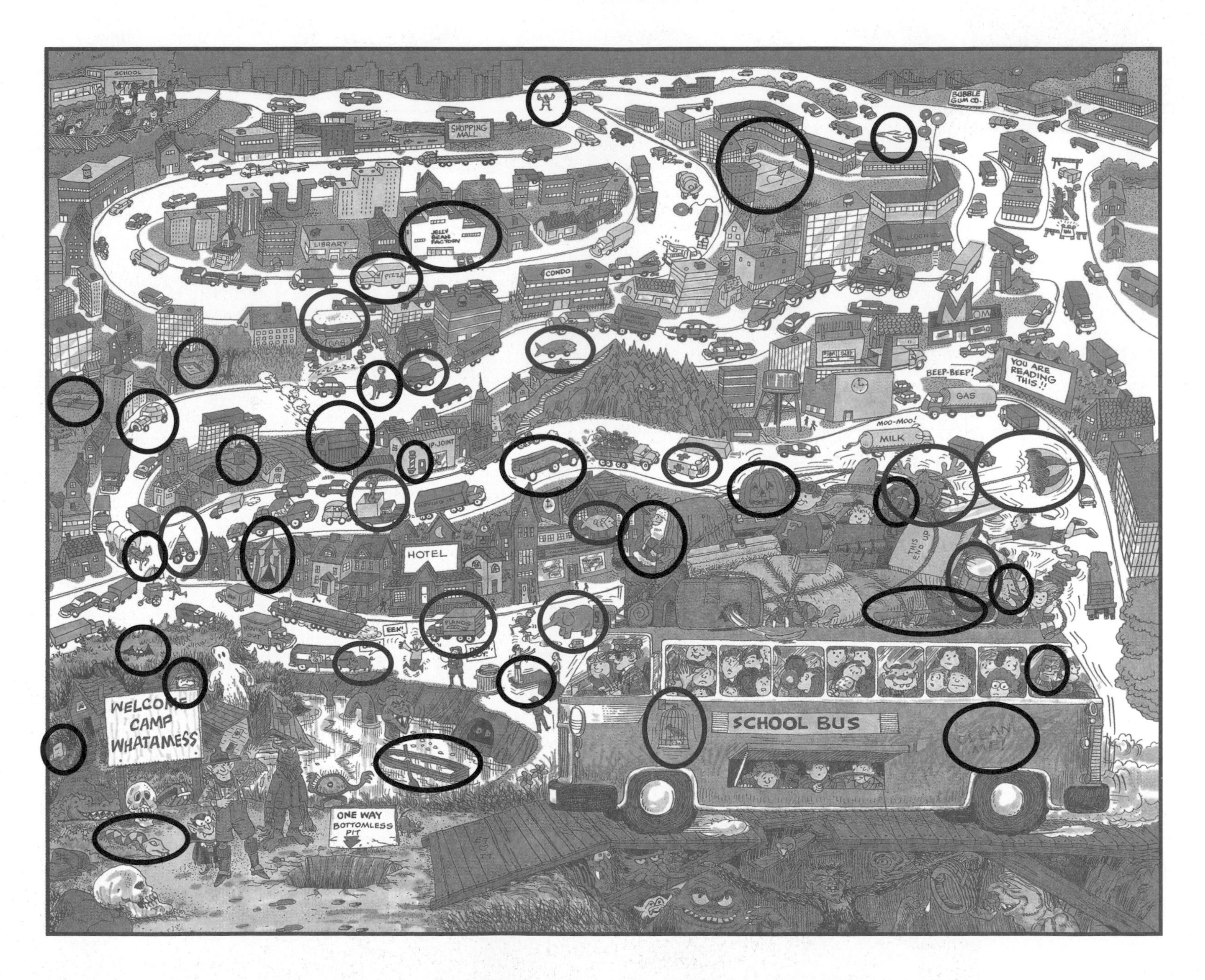

SCHOOL
SHOPPING MALL
BUBBLE GUM CO.
JELLY BEAN FACTORY
LIBRARY
PIZZA
CONDO
GAS
BALLOON CO.
YOU ARE READING THIS!!
BEEP-BEEP!
GAS
MOO-MOO!
MILK
HOTEL
THIS END UP
EEK!
PIANOS
WELCOME CAMP WHATAMESS
SCHOOL BUS
CLEAN ME!
ONE WAY BOTTOMLESS PIT

SEARCH & FIND® at the Circus Parade

- ☐ Bass drum
- ☐ Bone
- ☐ Broom
- ☐ Candle
- ☐ Carriage
- ☐ Cowboys (4)
- ☐ Crown
- ☐ Elephants (4)
- ☐ "Enter"
- ☐ Flags (6)
- ☐ Gorilla
- ☐ Hole
- ☐ Juggler
- ☐ Lion
- ☐ Net
- ☐ Plates (7)
- ☐ Police officers (2)
- ☐ Sad face
- ☐ Superhero
- ☐ Tents (7)
- ☐ Umbrellas (3)
- ☐ Unicorn
- ☐ Unicycle
- ☐ Upside-down sign
- ☐ Whistle
- ☐ Witch

Answers on the back.

ANSWERS

POST NO BILLS
NO PARKING
THIS END UP
NOT WET PAINT
SOMETHING IS WRONG HERE!
WHEN DO WE EAT?
I WANT TO GO TO TH ZO
I WANT TO DO THAT.
FOR RENT
YE OLD TENT
A FLYING SAUCER
NEXT LAUNCH 5 MINUTES
NEAT-O!
CAN DO AT!
GOO!
EXIT
ENTER
HI, BOBBY.
I LOVE IT!
I'M GOING TO RUN AWAY WITH THE CIRCUS.
GOOD!
SAY GOODBYE TO THAT CLOWN.
HI, MOM!
I AM NOT A CLOWN.
HERE CO CLE HARRY!
THIS IS DULL!
WHERE'S LISA?
I SHOULD HAVE BECOME A BATON
I'M DOG TOO.
I LOVE THE CLOWN'S HAIR STYLE.

SEARCH & FIND®
on the
Farm
BEGINNERS
Tractor
Police officer
Chicken
Eskimo
Goat
Piggy bank
Turtle
Bed
Fox
Basketball hoop
Rooster
Surfer
Turkey
Boat
Cactus
Cave
Clouds (3)
Covered wagon
Deer
Donkey
"Don't Stop" sign
Egg
Elephant
"Finish" line
Ghost
Giant pumpkin
"Grade A"
Log pile
Message in a bottle
Net
Periscope
Pitchfork
Prisoner
Scarecrows (5)
Scuba diver
"Stop" sign
Tent
"TV Dinners"
Worm
Answers on the back.
I HOPE THE FURNACE ISN'T ON!
CANNED FOODS
TV DINNERS
BUBBLE GUM
THIS IS BETTER ON WATER!
TRUCK FARM
FRESH APPLE CIDER
DO NOT PICK
NO EXIT
FROZEN FOODS
JUNK FOOD
WHERE AM I ?
FAST FOOD
POP CORN
DON'T STOP
I'M GOING BACK!
SLOW FOOD
FARM ANIMALS ONLY
I RESENT THAT!
BIG APPLE APPLES
YUM!
ME TOO!
WHAT DOES "BAA" MEAN?
HEY, MOM!
NO MOO. I QUIT.
THEY ARE ALMOST READY TO HARVEST!
CANDY CANES
NO KITES ALLOWED IN THIS PICTURE
MUD IS BEAUTIFUL.
I CAUGHT THE FOX WATCHING TV IN THE HEN HOUSE!
I SHOULD HAVE LEFT WITH MY PAL DONALD.
CONTAINER FARM
I FEEL LIKE JOGGING!
THIS IS A REAL TURKEY.
SO AM I.
HAS ANYONE SEEN LISA?
EEK!
I ♥ MUD.
I'M GOING TO BUTT IN.
I'M SCARED!
FINISH
GLUB!
I'M LOST!
HEE HAW!
I'M GOING TO STOP FARMING!
SUMMER

ANSWERS

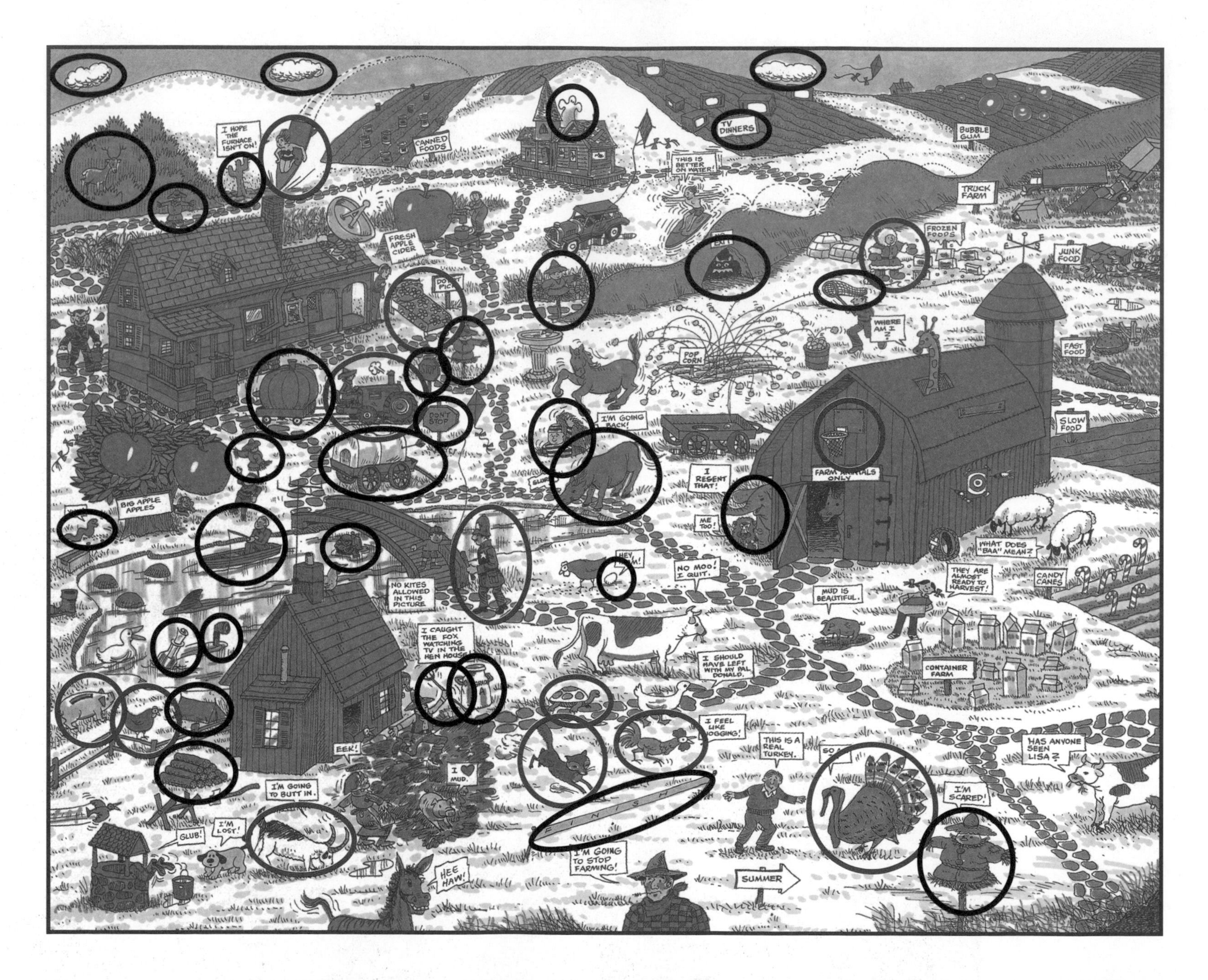

I HOPE THE FURNACE ISN'T ON!
CANNED FOODS
TV DINNERS
THIS IS BETTER ON WATER!
BUBBLE GUM
TRUCK FARM
FRESH APPLE CIDER
FROZEN FOODS
JUNK FOOD
WHERE AM I?
POP CORN
FAST FOOD
SLOW FOOD
I'M GOING BACK!
DON'T STOP
I RESENT THAT!
ME TOO!
BIG APPLE APPLES
WHAT DOES "BAA" MEAN?
NO KITES ALLOWED IN THIS PICTURE
NO MOO! I QUIT.
MUD IS BEAUTIFUL.
THEY ARE ALMOST READY TO HARVEST!
CANDY CANES
I CAUGHT THE FOX WATCHING TV IN THE HEN HOUSE!
I SHOULD HAVE LEFT WITH MY PAL DONALD.
CONTAINER FARM
THIS IS A REAL TURKEY.
HAS ANYONE SEEN LISA?
EEK!
I ♥ MUD.
I'M GOING TO BUTT IN.
I'M SCARED!
GLUB!
I'M LOST!
HEE HAW!
I'M GOING TO STOP FARMING!
SUMMER
FINISH

SEARCH & FIND® at the Flea Market

- ☐ Birdcages (2)
- ☐ Court jester
- ☐ Cowboy hat
- ☐ Crown
- ☐ Elephant
- ☐ Elf
- ☐ Fishing hook
- ☐ Football
- ☐ French horn
- ☐ Frogs (2)
- ☐ Golf club
- ☐ Horse
- ☐ Map
- ☐ Monster
- ☐ Necklace
- ☐ Old tire
- ☐ Paintbrush
- ☐ Pear
- ☐ Records (8)
- ☐ Sailor
- ☐ Scuba diver
- ☐ Shopping bag
- ☐ Spinning wheel
- ☐ Telephone booth
- ☐ Train conductor
- ☐ Wheelbarrow

Answers on the back.

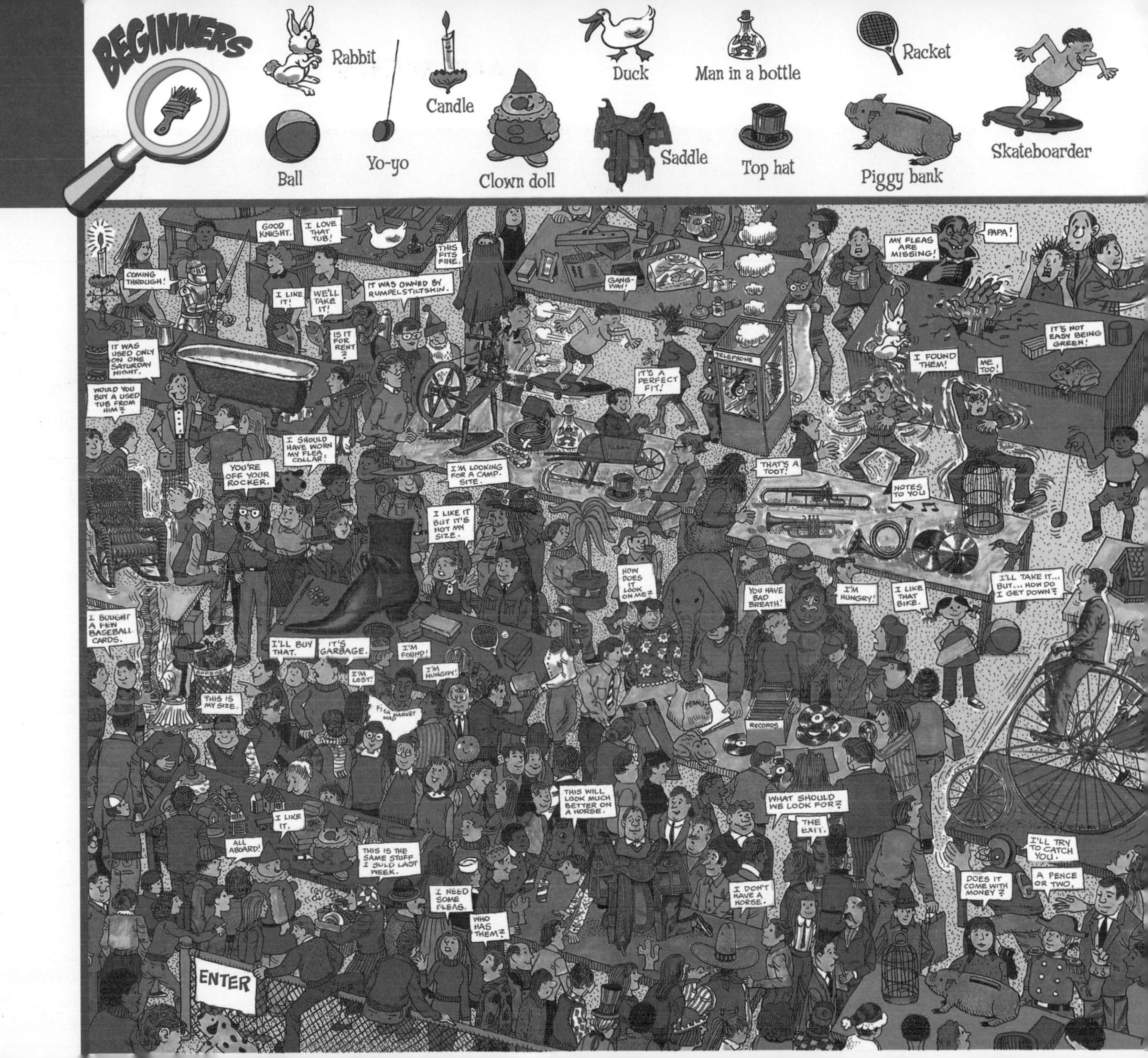

ANSWERS

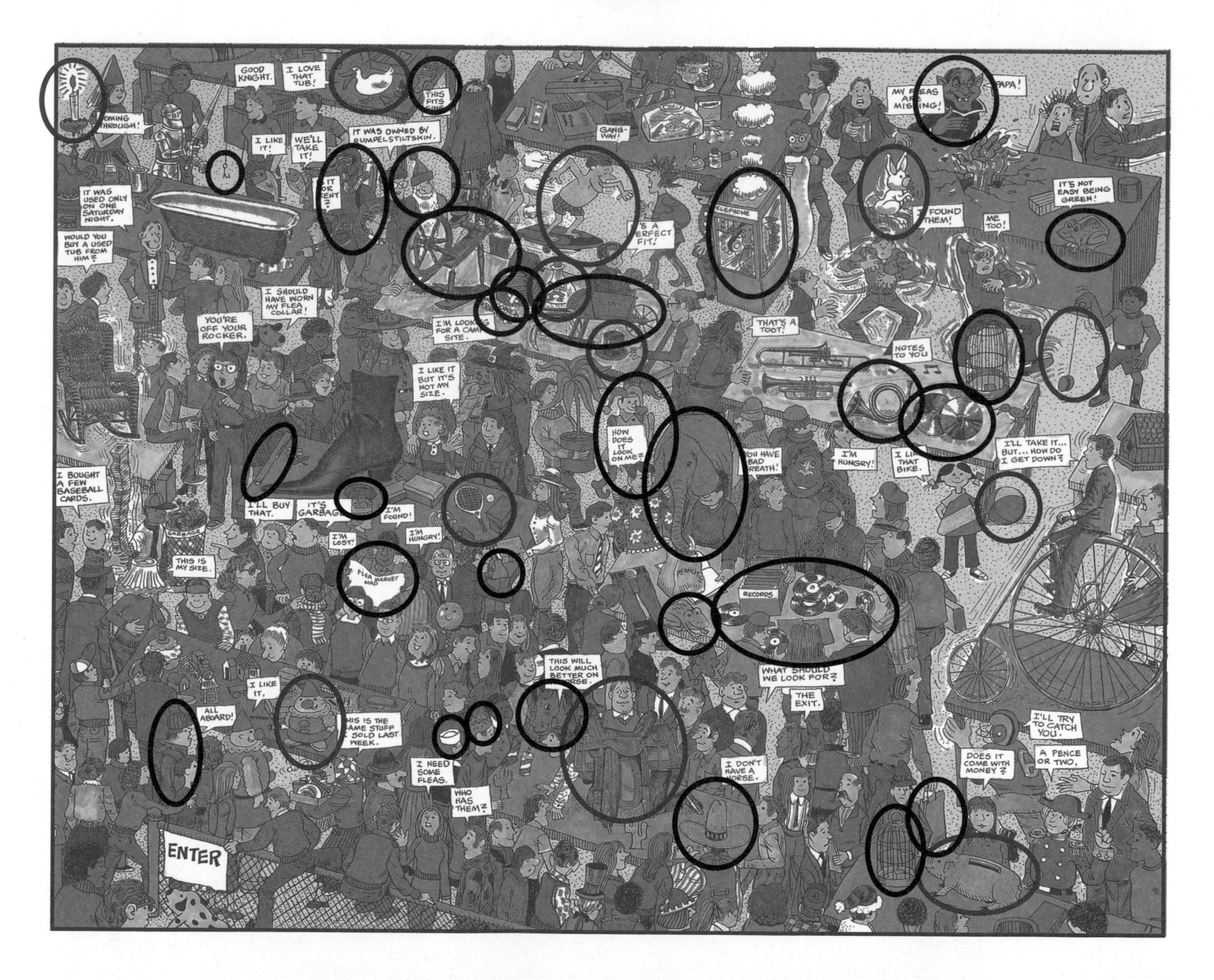

GOOD KNIGHT.
I LOVE THAT TUB!
I LIKE IT!
WE'LL TAKE IT!
IT WAS OWNED BY RUMPELSTILTSKIN.
GANG-WAY!
IT WAS USED ONLY ON ONE SATURDAY NIGHT.
WOULD YOU BUY A USED TUB FROM HIM?
I SHOULD HAVE WORN MY FLEA COLLAR!
YOU'RE OFF YOUR ROCKER.
I LIKE IT BUT IT'S NOT MY SIZE.
PAPA!
IT'S NOT EASY BEING GREEN!
ME TOO!
TELEPHONE
THAT'S A TOOT!
NOTES TO YOU
I'LL TAKE IT... BUT... HOW DO I GET DOWN?
I'M HUNGRY!
HOW DOES IT LOOK ON ME?
I BOUGHT A FEW BASEBALL CARDS.
I'LL BUY THAT.
I'M FOUND!
I'M LOST!
I'M HUNGRY!
GARBAGE
THIS IS MY SIZE.
FLEA MARKET MAP
I LIKE IT.
ALL ABOARD!
THIS WILL LOOK MUCH BETTER ON
I NEED SOME FLEAS.
WHO HAS THEM?
ENTER
PEANUTS
RECORDS
WHAT SHOULD WE LOOK FOR?
THE EXIT.
I DON'T HAVE A
I'LL TRY TO CATCH YOU.
DOES IT COME WITH MONEY?
A PENCE OR TWO.

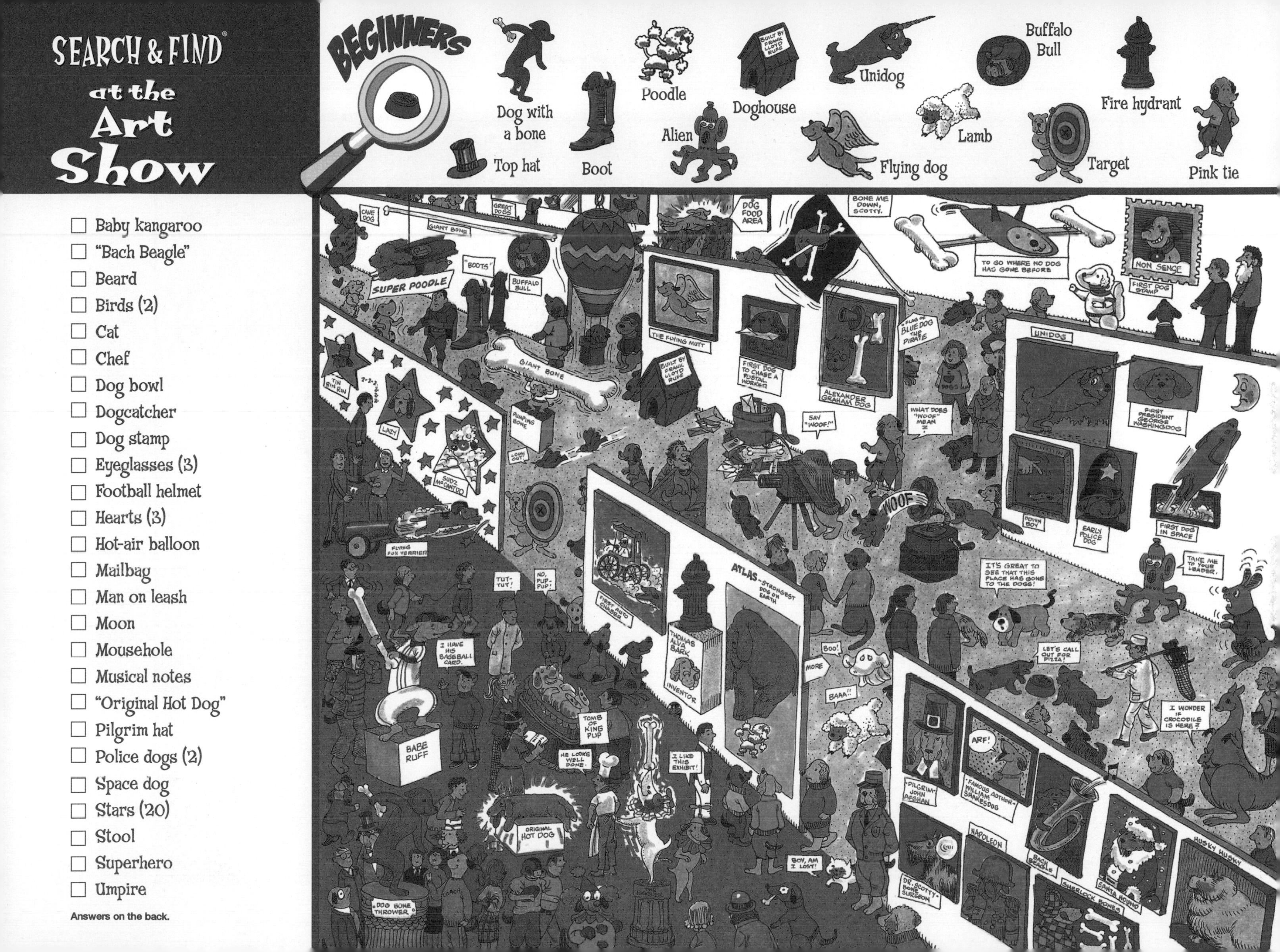
SEARCH & FIND®
at the
Art
Show
BEGINNERS
Dog with a bone
Top hat
Boot
Poodle
Alien
Doghouse
BUILT BY FRANK LLOYD RUFF
Unidog
Flying dog
Lamb
Buffalo Bull
Target
Fire hydrant
Pink tie
Baby kangaroo
"Bach Beagle"
Beard
Birds (2)
Cat
Chef
Dog bowl
Dogcatcher
Dog stamp
Eyeglasses (3)
Football helmet
Hearts (3)
Hot-air balloon
Mailbag
Man on leash
Moon
Mousehole
Musical notes
"Original Hot Dog"
Pilgrim hat
Police dogs (2)
Space dog
Stars (20)
Stool
Superhero
Umpire
Answers on the back.
CAVE DOG
GIANT BONE
GREAT DOGS
DOG FOOD AREA
BONE ME DOWN, SCOTTY.
TO GO WHERE NO DOG HAS GONE BEFORE
NON SENSE
FIRST DOG STAMP
SUPER POODLE
"BOOTS"
BUFFALO BULL
THE FLYING MUTT
FIRST DOG TO CHASE A POSTAL WORKER
ALEXANDER GRAHAM DOG
FLAG OF BLUE DOG THE PIRATE
UNIDOG
FIRST PRESIDENT GEORGE WASHINGDOG
GIANT BONE
PUMPING BONE
LAZY
SUDZ McCANDO
SAY "WOOF!"
WHAT DOES "WOOF" MEAN ?
WOOF
DOWN BOY
EARLY POLICE DOG
FIRST DOG IN SPACE
FLYING FOX TERRIER
TUT-TUT!
NO, PUP-PUP!
FIRST AUTO CHASER
ATLAS – STRONGEST DOG ON EARTH
THOMAS ALVA BARK INVENTOR
IT'S GREAT TO SEE THAT THIS PLACE HAS GONE TO THE DOGS!
TAKE ME TO YOUR LEADER.
I HAVE HIS BASEBALL CARD.
BOO!
MORE
LET'S CALL OUT FOR PIZZA!
BAAA!!
I WONDER IF CROCODILE IS HERE ?
BABE RUFF
TOMB OF KING PUP
HE LOOKS WELL DONE.
I LIKE THIS EXHIBIT!
ARF!
PILGRIM JOHN AFGHAN
FAMOUS AUTHOR WILLIAM SHAKESDOG
ORIGINAL HOT DOG
NAPOLEON
BACH BEAGLE
SANTA HOUND
HUSKY HUSKY
SHERLOCK BONES
BOY, AM I LOST!
DR. SCOTTY-BONE SURGEON
DOG BONE THROWER

ANSWERS

CAVE DOG
GIANT BONE
GREAT DOGS
DOG FOOD AREA
BONE ME DOWN, SCOTTY.
TO GO WHERE NO DOG HAS GONE BEFORE
NON SENSE
FIRST DOG STAMP
SUPER POODLE
"BOOTS"
BUFFALO BILL
GIANT BONE
BUILT BY FRANK LLOYD RUFF
FIRST DOG TO CHASE A POSTAL WORKER
ALEXANDER GRAHAM DOG
FLAG OF BLUE DOG THE PIRATE
UNIDOG
FIRST PRESIDENT GEORGE WASHINGDOG
SAY "WOOF!"
WHAT DOES "WOOF" MEAN ?
WOOF
PUMPING BONE
LOOK OUT!
MCCANTDO
DOWN BOY
EARLY POLICE DOGS
FIRST DOG IN SPACE
TAKE ME TO YOUR LEADER.
FLYING FOX TERRIER
TUT-TUT!
NO, PUP, PUP!
FIRST AUTO CHASER
THOMAS ALVA BARK
INVENTOR
ATLAS - STRONGEST DOG ON EARTH
IT'S GREAT TO SEE THAT THIS PLACE HAS GONE TO THE DOGS!
I HAVE HIS BASEBALL CARD.
BOO!
MORE
LET'S CALL OUT FOR PIZZA!
I WONDER IF THE CROCODILE IS HERE ?
BABE RUFF
TOMB OF KING PUP
HE LOOKS WELL DONE.
I LIKE THIS EXHIBIT!
ARF!
"PILGRIM" JOHN AFGHAN
"FAMOUS AUTHOR" WILLIAM SHAKESDOG
ORIGINAL HOT DOG
NAPOLEON
BACH BEAGLE
HUSKY HUSKY
BOY, AM I LOST!
DR. SCOTTY BONE SURGEON
SHERLOCK BONES
SANTA HOUND
"DOG BONE THROWER"

SEARCH & FIND®
at the Dog Olympics

- ☐ Basketball
- ☐ Bowling ball
- ☐ Broom
- ☐ Clipboard
- ☐ Diving board
- ☐ Dog-food bowls (2)
- ☐ Falling skater
- ☐ Fencing swords (2)
- ☐ Fishing pole
- ☐ Football players (3)
- ☐ Golf tee
- ☐ Hat with propeller
- ☐ "Hi, Mom"
- ☐ Home plate
- ☐ Ice skates (14)
- ☐ Karate dog
- ☐ Pail
- ☐ Paper airplane
- ☐ Ping-Pong paddle
- ☐ Pitcher
- ☐ Pole-vaulter
- ☐ Sleeping dogs (2)
- ☐ Soccer ball
- ☐ Target
- ☐ Tennis racket
- ☐ Top hat

Answers on the back.

ANSWERS

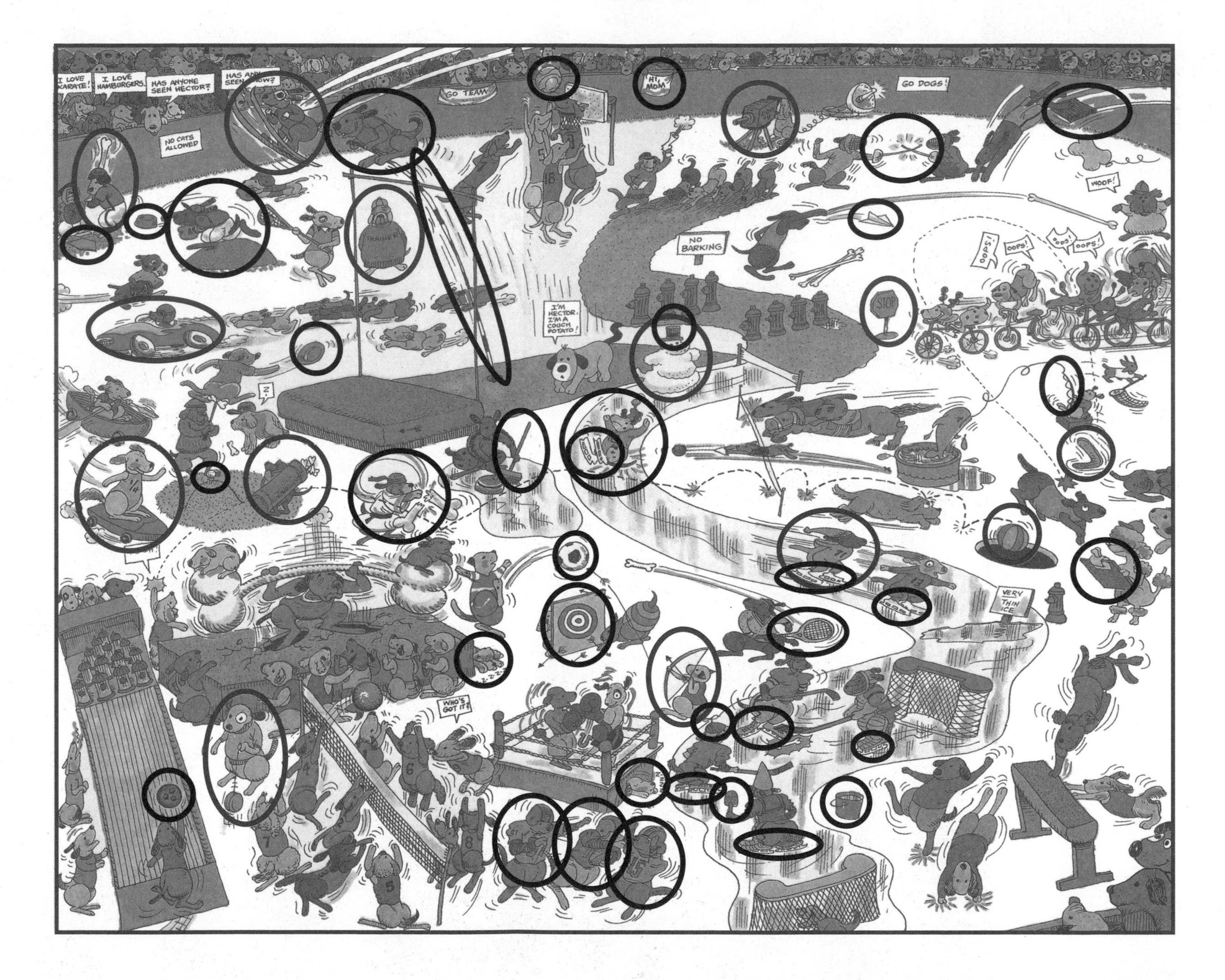

I LOVE KARATE!
I LOVE HAMBURGERS.
HAS ANYONE SEEN HECTOR?
GO TEAM
HI MOM
GO DOGS!
NO CATS ALLOWED
TRAINER
WOOF!
NO BARKING
OOPS!
OOPS!
OOPS!
OOPS!
STOP
I'M HECTOR. I'M A COUCH POTATO!
VERY THIN ICE
WHO'S GOT IT?

SEARCH & FIND® at the Amusement Park

- ☐ All-north weather vane
- ☐ Archer
- ☐ Baseball
- ☐ Cheese
- ☐ Clock
- ☐ Clowns (3)
- ☐ Cowboys (2)
- ☐ Crocodile
- ☐ Crooked chimney
- ☐ Diving board
- ☐ Dollar sign
- ☐ Fishing pole
- ☐ Heads without bodies (2)
- ☐ "House of Horrors"
- ☐ Ice block
- ☐ Manhole
- ☐ Moon
- ☐ Mousehole
- ☐ Snowman
- ☐ Tied-up man
- ☐ Tombstones (3)
- ☐ "Tunnel of Love"
- ☐ TV antenna
- ☐ Umbrella
- ☐ Witch

Answers on the back.

ANSWERS

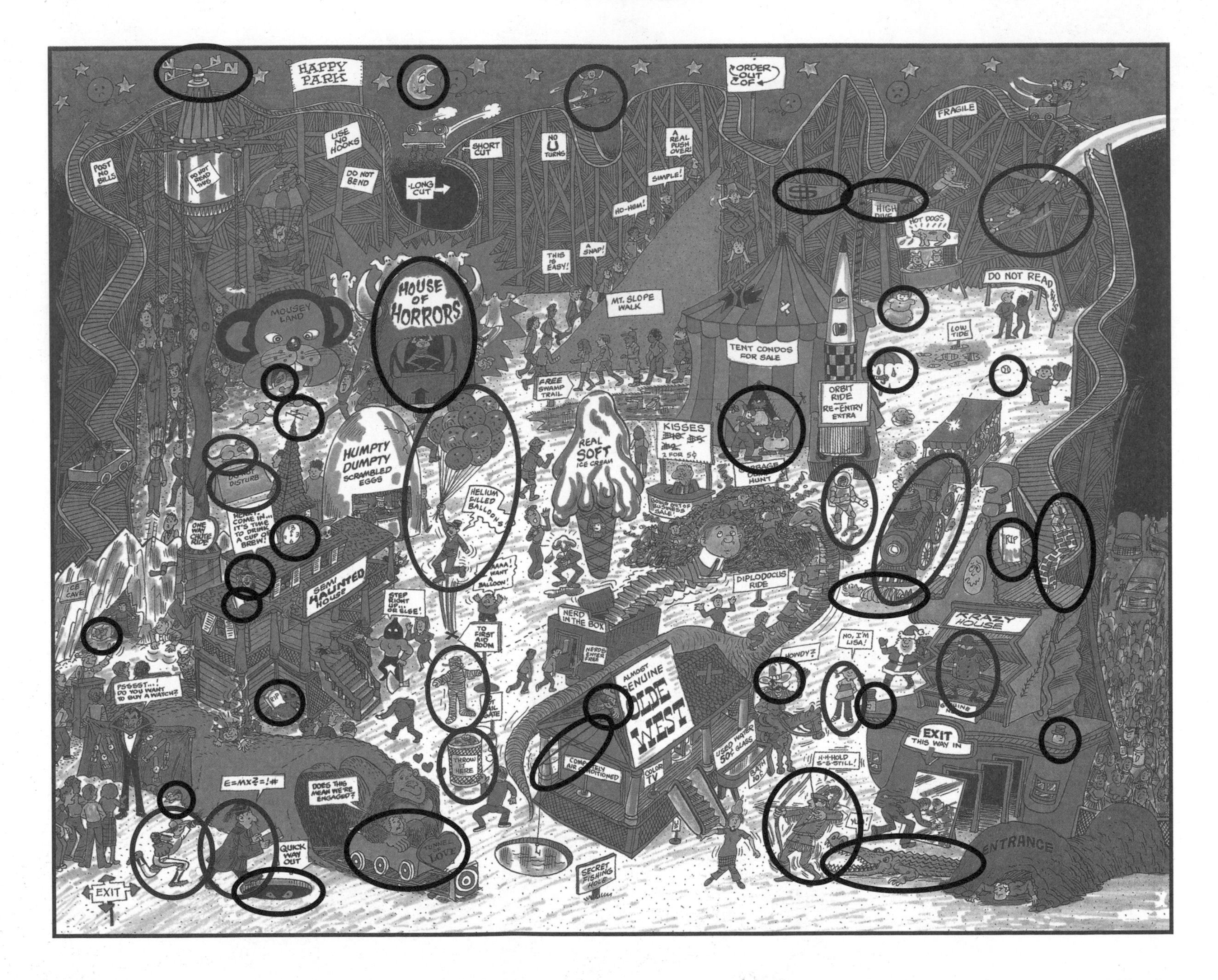

HAPPY PARK
ORDER OUT OF
FRAGILE
USE NO HOOKS
SHORT CUT
NO U TURNS
A REAL PUSH OVER!
POST NO BILLS
DO NOT READ THIS
DO NOT BEND
LONG CUT
SIMPLE!
HO-HUM!
HIGH DIVE
HOT DOGS
THIS IS EASY!
A SNAP!
DO NOT READ THIS
MOUSEY LAND
HOUSE OF HORRORS
MT. SLOPE WALK
TENT CONDOS FOR SALE
LOW TIDE
FREE SWAMP TRAIL
ORBIT RIDE
RE-ENTRY EXTRA
KISSES
2 FOR 5¢
HUMPTY DUMPTY SCRAMBLED EGGS
REAL SOFT ICE CREAM
HELIUM FILLED BALLOONS
GARBAGE HUNT
GOING OUT OF BUSINESS SALE!
DO NOT DISTURB
SEMI HAUNTED HOUSE
DIPLODOCUS RIDE
ICE CAVE
STEP RIGHT UP... OR ELSE!
MAAA! I WANT A BALLOON!
NERD IN THE BOX
NERDS ENTER FREE
TO FIRST AID ROOM
KRAZY HOUSE
NO, I'M LISA!
HOWDY!
ALMOST GENUINE OLDE WEST
PSSSST...! DO YOU WANT TO BUY A WATCH?
RIP
THROW IT HERE
COMPLETELY AIR CONDITIONED
COLOR TV
USED WATER 50¢ GLASS
EXIT THIS WAY IN
H-H-HOLD S-S-STILL!
E=MX²=!#
DOES THIS MEAN WE'RE ENGAGED?
QUICK WAY OUT
TUNNEL OF LOVE
SECRET FISHING HOLE
ENTRANCE
EXIT

SEARCH & FIND®

with the Dog Busters

- ☐ Balloon
- ☐ Bones (13)
- ☐ Bridge
- ☐ "Brooklyn"
- ☐ Broom
- ☐ Cage
- ☐ Clown
- ☐ Crane
- ☐ "Dog Hideout" sign
- ☐ Dogs in tree (2)
- ☐ Fish (4)
- ☐ Hollow log
- ☐ Jack-o'-lantern
- ☐ Ladders (3)
- ☐ Lamppost
- ☐ Manhole cover
- ☐ Mice (2)
- ☐ Net
- ☐ Old tire
- ☐ Pizza box
- ☐ "Poison Ivy"
- ☐ Saddle
- ☐ Sailboat
- ☐ Siren
- ☐ Taxi
- ☐ Tightrope walker

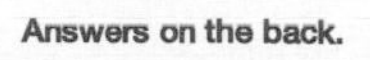

Answers on the back.

ANSWERS

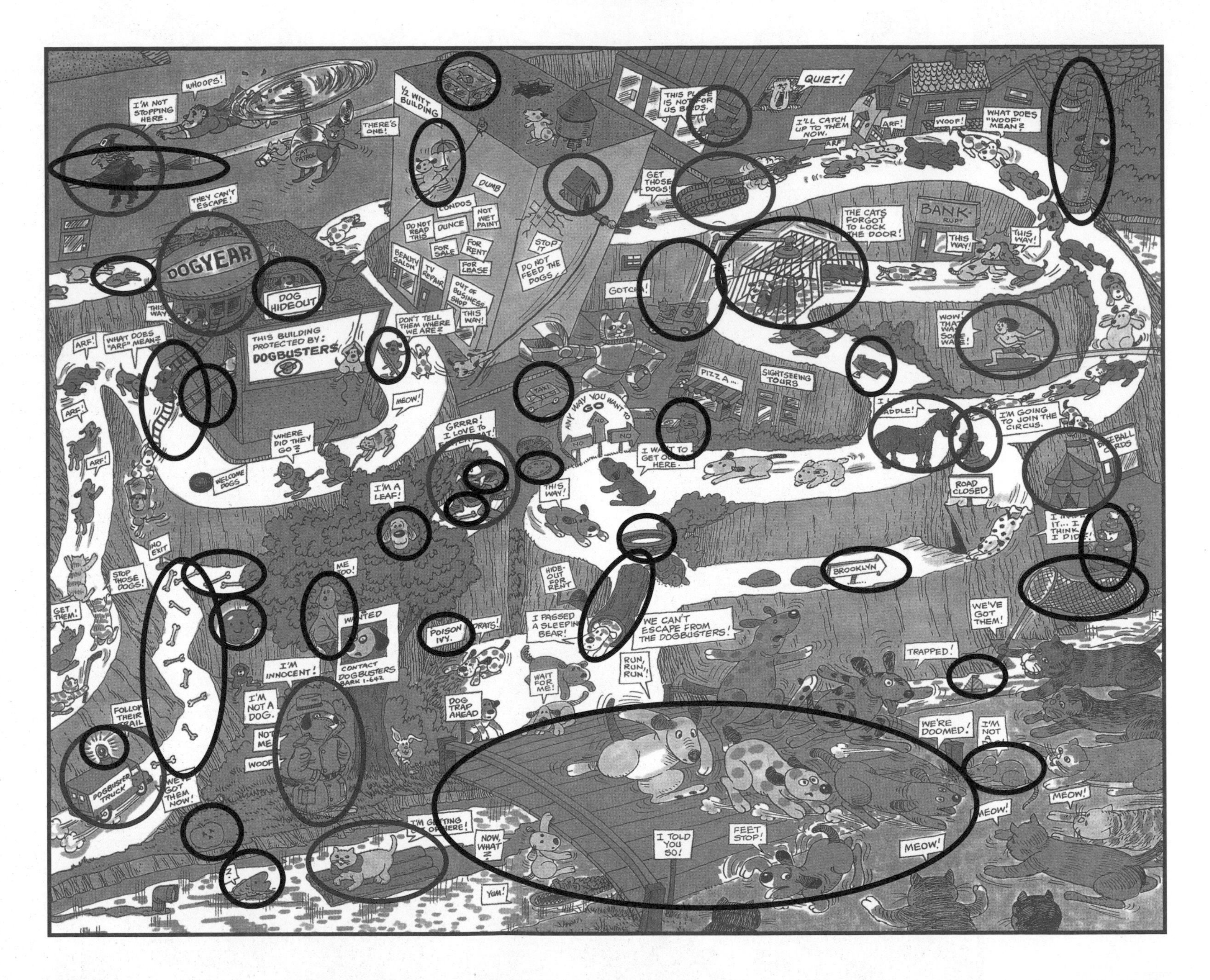

WHOOPS!
I'M NOT STOPPING HERE.
CAT PATROL
THERE'S ONE!
½ WITT BUILDING
QUIET!
I'LL CATCH UP TO THEM NOW.
ARF!
WOOF!
WHAT DOES "WOOF" MEAN?
GET THOSE DOGS!
DUMB
CONDOS
DO NOT READ THIS
DUNCE
NOT WET PAINT
FOR SALE
FOR RENT
FOR LEASE
BEAUTY SALON
TV REPAIR
OUT OF BUSINESS SHOP
THIS WAY!
DON'T TELL THEM WHERE WE ARE?
STOP IT
DO NOT FEED THE DOGS
THEY CAN'T ESCAPE!
DOGYEAR
DOG HIDEOUT
THIS BUILDING PROTECTED BY: DOGBUSTERS
THE CATS FORGOT TO LOCK THE DOOR!
BANK-RUPT
THIS WAY!
THIS WAY!
GOTCHA!
PIZZA...
SIGHTSEEING TOURS
ARF!
WHAT DOES "ARF" MEAN?
MEOW!
ANY WAY YOU WANT TO GO
NO
NO
I'M GOING TO JOIN THE CIRCUS.
WHERE DID THEY GO?
WELCOME DOGS
ARF!
ARF!
I'M A LEAF!
THIS WAY!
ROAD CLOSED
BROOKLYN
NO EXIT
STOP THOSE DOGS!
GET THEM!
ME TOO!
WANTED
CONTACT DOGBUSTERS BARK 1-642
POISON IVY.
RATS!
HIDE-OUT FOR RENT
WE CAN'T ESCAPE FROM THE DOGBUSTERS!
WE'VE GOT THEM!
TRAPPED!
I'M INNOCENT!
I'M NOT A DOG.
WAIT FOR ME!
RUN, RUN, RUN.
DOG TRAP AHEAD
WE'RE DOOMED!
WOOF
DOGBUSTER TRUCK
NOW, WHAT?
I TOLD YOU SO!
FEET STOP!
MEOW!
MEOW!
YUM!

SEARCH & FIND® at the Watering Hole

- ☐ Baby bird
- ☐ Balloons (3)
- ☐ Birdcage
- ☐ Clothespins (2)
- ☐ Coconuts (4)
- ☐ Donkey
- ☐ Duck
- ☐ Feather
- ☐ Fish (4)
- ☐ Headband
- ☐ Hippo
- ☐ Leopard
- ☐ Lions (2)
- ☐ Log
- ☐ Lollipop
- ☐ Octopus
- ☐ Pig
- ☐ Ping-Pong paddle
- ☐ Pink elephant
- ☐ Rhinoceros
- ☐ Robot
- ☐ Snake
- ☐ Tin can
- ☐ Television
- ☐ UFO
- ☐ Worm

Answers on the back.

ANSWERS

?
I'M JOE OF THE JUNGLE.
I'M LOST!
I NEVER SAW ANYTHING LIKE THAT WHEN I WAS ON TOP OF THE EMPIRE STATE BUILDING!
HEE-HAW!
I'D BETTER GET ON BOARD!
JUNGLE TOURS
EEEK! A JUNGLE U.F.O.!
THIS PLACE IS NOT FOR ME!
STRANGE LOOKING.
I WISH I COULD FLY!
I'D BETTER GO HOME!
I'D BETTER TRICK OR TREAT!
?
?
FOR RENT
I'M HUNGRY.
?
AHOY!
?
A FISH OUT OF WATER!
THAT'S NO FISH!
IT'S NOT A TURTLE EITHER!
WHAT IS IT?
IT'S NOT A WART HOG LIKE ME!
UGH!! CLEAN WATER!

SEARCH & FIND®
Dogs in Space

- ☐ Bench
- ☐ Blimp
- ☐ Bone smokestack
- ☐ Boxing glove
- ☐ Bus
- ☐ Cars (3)
- ☐ Diving board
- ☐ "Dog Catcher"
- ☐ "Dog Fish"
- ☐ "Dog Paddle"
- ☐ "Dog Wood"
- ☐ Earth
- ☐ Graduate
- ☐ Heart with arrow
- ☐ Hot dog
- ☐ Mailbag
- ☐ Old tire
- ☐ Pizza
- ☐ "Pluto"
- ☐ Pup in a cup
- ☐ Rescue dog
- ☐ Roller coaster
- ☐ Space map
- ☐ Star with tail
- ☐ Top hat
- ☐ Trash can

Answers on the back.

ANSWERS

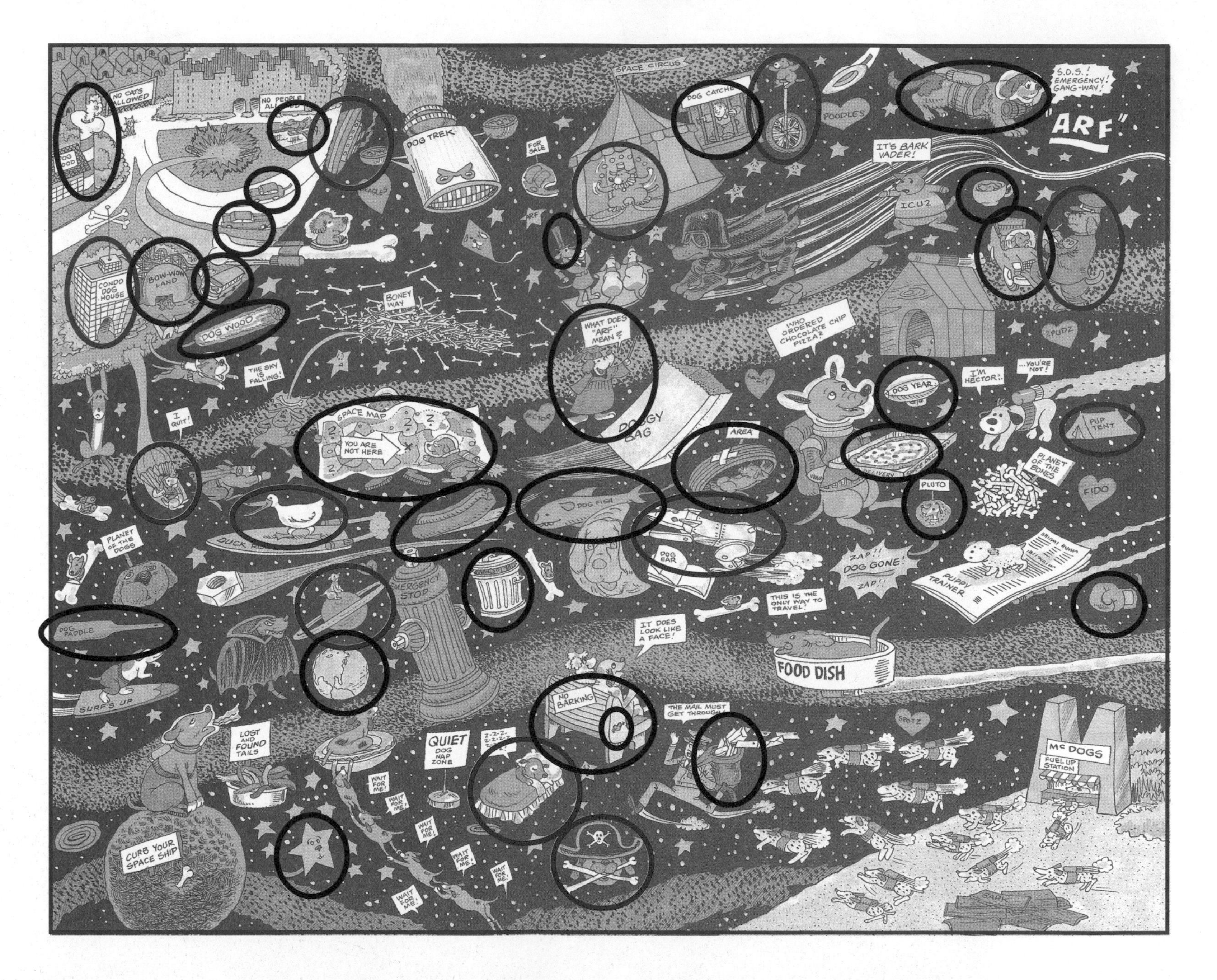

NO CATS ALLOWED
NO PEOPLE ALLOWED
DOG FOOD
DOG TREK
SPACE CIRCUS
POODLES
S.O.S.! EMERGENCY! GANG-WAY!
"ARF"
IT'S BARK VADER!
FOR SALE
EAGLES
ARF
ICU2
CONDO DOG HOUSE
BOW-WOW LAND
DOG WOOD
BONEY WAY
2PUDZ
WHO ORDERED CHOCOLATE CHIP PIZZA?
WHAT DOES "ARF" MEAN?
DOGGY BAG
LAZY
HECTOR
I'M HECTOR!
...YOU'RE NOT!
DOG YEAR
PUP TENT
THE SKY IS FALLING!
I QUIT!
SPACE MAP
YOU ARE NOT HERE
AREA
DELIVERY
PLANET OF THE BONES
PLUTO
FIDO
DOG FISH
DOG EAR
PLANET OF THE DOGS
EMERGENCY STOP
ZAP!! DOG GONE! ZAP!!
PUPPY TRAINER
DOG PADDLE
THIS IS THE ONLY WAY TO TRAVEL!
IT DOES LOOK LIKE A FACE!
FOOD DISH
SURF'S UP
NO BARKING
THE MAIL MUST GET THROUGH!
SPOTZ
LOST AND FOUND TAILS
QUIET DOG NAP ZONE
WAIT FOR ME!
WAIT FOR ME!
WAIT FOR ME!
WAIT FOR ME!
WAIT FOR ME!
WAIT FOR ME.
McDOGS
FUEL UP STATION
CURB YOUR SPACE SHIP
BARK

SEARCH & FIND®
at the
Yum-Yum
Emporium
BEGINNERS
Hot dog
Hot chocolate
"A happy customer"
Costume
Mailbox
Frankie
Toupee
Cowboy
Birdcage
NO EXIT
Sign
Ice-cream cone
Salt shaker
Alien
Baseball cap
Bib
Book
Booster seat
Briefcase
Crown
Crutch
Cupcake
Duck
Eyeglasses (7)
Eye patch
Food fight
Football player
Knight
Man with fingers in ears
Napkin dispensers (2)
Pearl necklaces (2)
Pig
Pizza
Rain slicker
Red bandanas (2)
Red hats (2)
Shark fin
Skulls (2)
Turtles (2)
Answers on the back.
YUM-YUM FAST FOOD EMPORIUM
NO EXIT
IF YOU DON'T SEE IT... YOU'RE LUCKY!
MYSTERY MEAL #1
DON'T BUY ME!
HOT DOG
EAT HERE 5 DAYS IN A ROW AND...
R.I.P.
SOUP OF THE DAY
REAL HOT CHOCOLATE
RUBBER DUCK
PURE JUNK FOOD
A HAPPY CUSTOMER
I'M IN A RUSH! I'VE GOT TO GET BACK TO WORK!!
DO WE HAVE A RESERVATION
I'LL HAVE EVERYTHING!
I WEAR A TIE... I'M THE MANAGER!
WHAT'S GOOD HERE?
THE TRAYS!
HOWDY, SHERIFF!
HOWDY, COOKIE!
DO TOUCH
KILLER FISH
THEY HAVE HOME COOKING!
THAT BAD!
I HOPE THEY DON'T RUN OUT OF FOOD!
YUM, YUM, YUM!
I'M ON MY LUNCH BREAK!
HOW DO I EAT WEARING THIS?
YOU CAN'T!
YOU'RE LUCKY!
UGH!
DOUBLE UGH!!
TRIPLE UGH!!!
THIS IS GOOD MATERIAL FOR A FOOD FIGHT!
FASTER FAST FOOD
YOU EAT LIKE A PIG!!
THANK YOU!
WHAT DID I ORDER?
GRRR! EAT! EAT!!
PASS THE SALT!
OK!
THEY DON'T HAVE "YUM-YUM" ON MY PLANET!
YOU'RE LUCKY!
IF I'M LUCKY I WON'T FIND A SPOT TO SIT DOWN AND EAT!
DO YOU LIKE PIZZA?

ANSWERS

YUM-YUM FAST FOOD EMPORIUM
NO EXIT
IF YOU DON'T SEE IT... YOU'RE LUCKY!
MYSTERY MEAL #1
DON'T BUY ME!
HOT DOG
EAT HERE 5 DAYS IN A ROW AND...
RIP
SOUP OF THE DAY
REAL HOT CHOCOLATE
RUBBER DUCK
PURE JUNK FOOD
HAPPY CUSTOMER
I'M IN A RUSH! I'VE GOT TO GET BACK TO WORK!!
DO WE HAVE A RESERVATION
I'LL HAVE EVERYTHING!
I WEAR A TIE... I'M THE MANAGER!
WHAT'S GOOD HERE?
THE TRAYS!
HOWDY, SHERIFF!
HOWDY, COOKIE!
DO TOUCH
KILLER FISH
THEY HAVE HOME COOKING!
THAT BAD!
I HOPE THEY DON'T RUN OUT OF FOOD!
YUM, YUM, YUM!
I'M ON MY LUNCH BREAK!
YOU CAN'T!
YOU'RE LUCKY!
UGH!
DOUBLE UGH!!
TRIPLE UGH!!!
HOW DO I EAT WEARING THIS?
FASTER FAST FOOD
YOU EAT LIKE A PIG!!
THANK YOU!
GRRR! EAT! EAT!!
PASS THE SALT!
OK!
THEY DON'T HAVE "YUM-YUM" ON MY PLANET!
YOU'RE LUCKY!
IF I'M LUCKY I WON'T FIND A SPOT TO SIT DOWN AND EAT!
DO YOU LIKE PIZZA?

SEARCH & FIND on Planet Maxxx
Asteroid for rent
Banana
Baseball
Birds (2)
Briefcase
Clipboard
Clocks (4)
Covered wagon
Duck
Football player
Fork
"Grandma"
Hamburger
Hammer
Helmet
Jump rope
Moon
Mushroom
Old tire
Paintbrush
Paper airplane
Pyramid
Radio
Star
Sunglasses
Tree
Answers on the back.
BEGINNERS
Broom
Elephant
Pizza
Hot dog
Flowerpot
Monkey
Skateboarder
Sled
Tepee
Space tank
Television set
Plumber's plunger
Snake
FOR SALE
SOLD
WHO ORDERED PIZZA?
CONDO FOR SALE
CONDO FOR SALE.
DISCO
HURRY!
DON'T FORGET YOUR PEANUT BUTTER SANDWICHES!
WAIT FOR ME!
SAY "HI" TO GRANNY.
SAY "HI" TO FLASH AND BUCK!
HAVE A NICE TRIP, LAURA!
TO GRANDMOTHER'S HOUSE WE GO!
LAURA BLASTS OFF AT 3 O'CLOCK!
I WANT TO GO TOO!
BRING BACK UNCLE SPOCK!
I WANT A PRO CONTRACT.
BRING BACK A TREKKIE!
BRING BACK A COOKIE!
BRING BACK SOME OF GRANNY'S SOUP.
I WANT TO GO HOME!
I WANT A CANOE.
DO YOU HAVE A CLEAN HANKIE?
I WANT SOME PEANUTS!
I WANT A REFEREE.
I WANT A FIRE HYDRANT.
BRING BACK SOME OIL!
GRANDMA, HERE COMES LAURA!
TAKE YOUR CAMERA!
DON'T FORGET THE FILM!
WHAT'S "SOUP"?
BRING BACK A FLOWER.
I WANT A VIDEO GAME!

ANSWERS

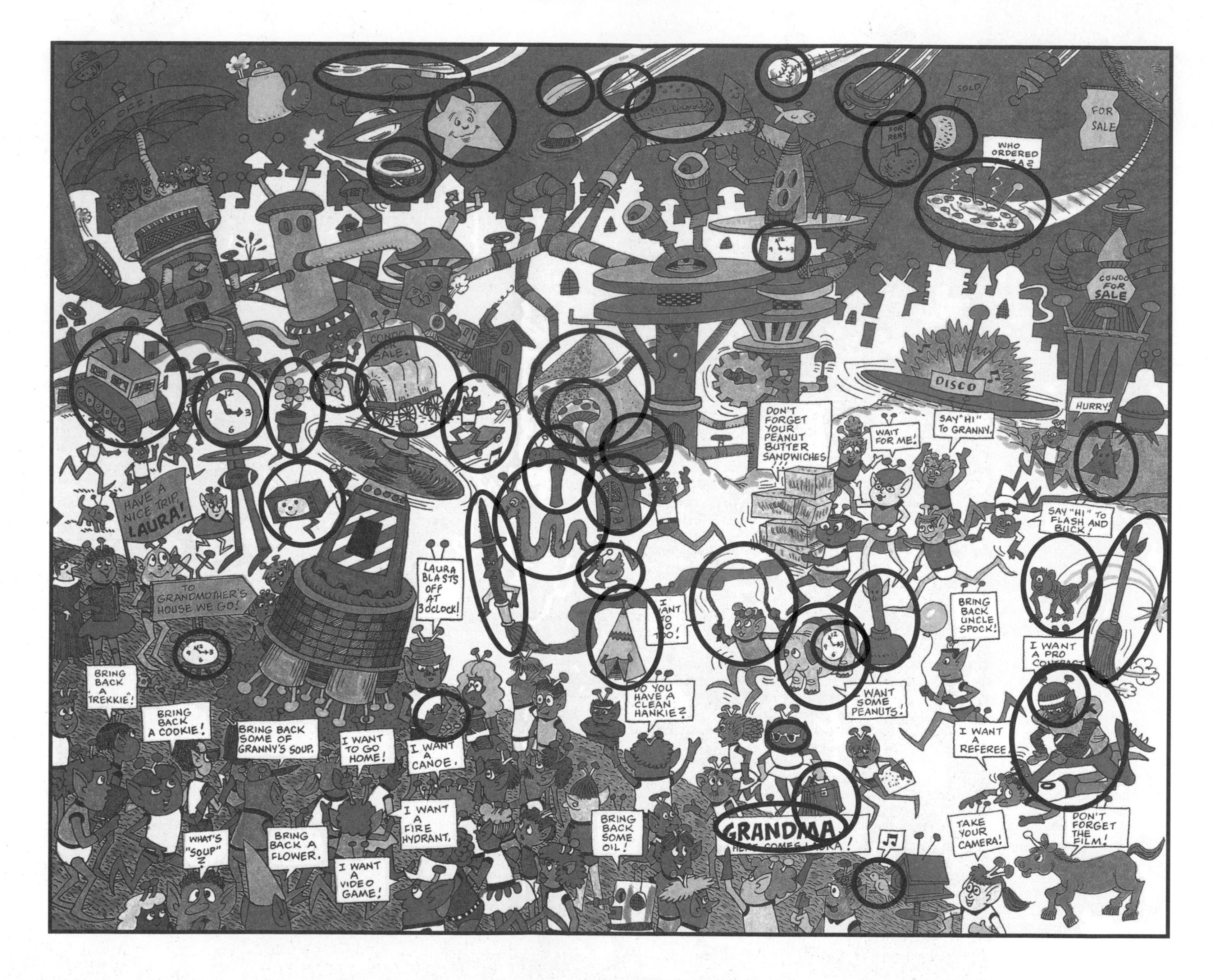

KEEP OFF!
FOR SALE
SOLD
FOR RENT
WHO ORDERED
CONDO FOR SALE
DISCO
HURRY!
DON'T FORGET YOUR PEANUT BUTTER SANDWICHES!!!
WAIT FOR ME!
SAY "HI" TO GRANNY.
SAY "HI" TO FLASH AND BUCK!
HAVE A NICE TRIP, LAURA!
TO GRANDMOTHER'S HOUSE WE GO!
LAURA BLASTS OFF AT 3 o'CLOCK!
I WANT TO GO TOO!
BRING BACK UNCLE SPOCK!
I WANT A PRO
DO YOU HAVE A CLEAN HANKIE?
I WANT SOME PEANUTS!
I WANT A REFEREE.
BRING BACK A "TREKKIE"!
BRING BACK A COOKIE!
BRING BACK SOME OF GRANNY'S SOUP.
I WANT TO GO HOME!
I WANT A CANOE.
I WANT A FIRE HYDRANT.
BRING BACK SOME OIL!
GRANDMA
TAKE YOUR CAMERA!
DON'T FORGET THE FILM!
WHAT'S "SOUP"?
BRING BACK A FLOWER.
I WANT A VIDEO GAME!

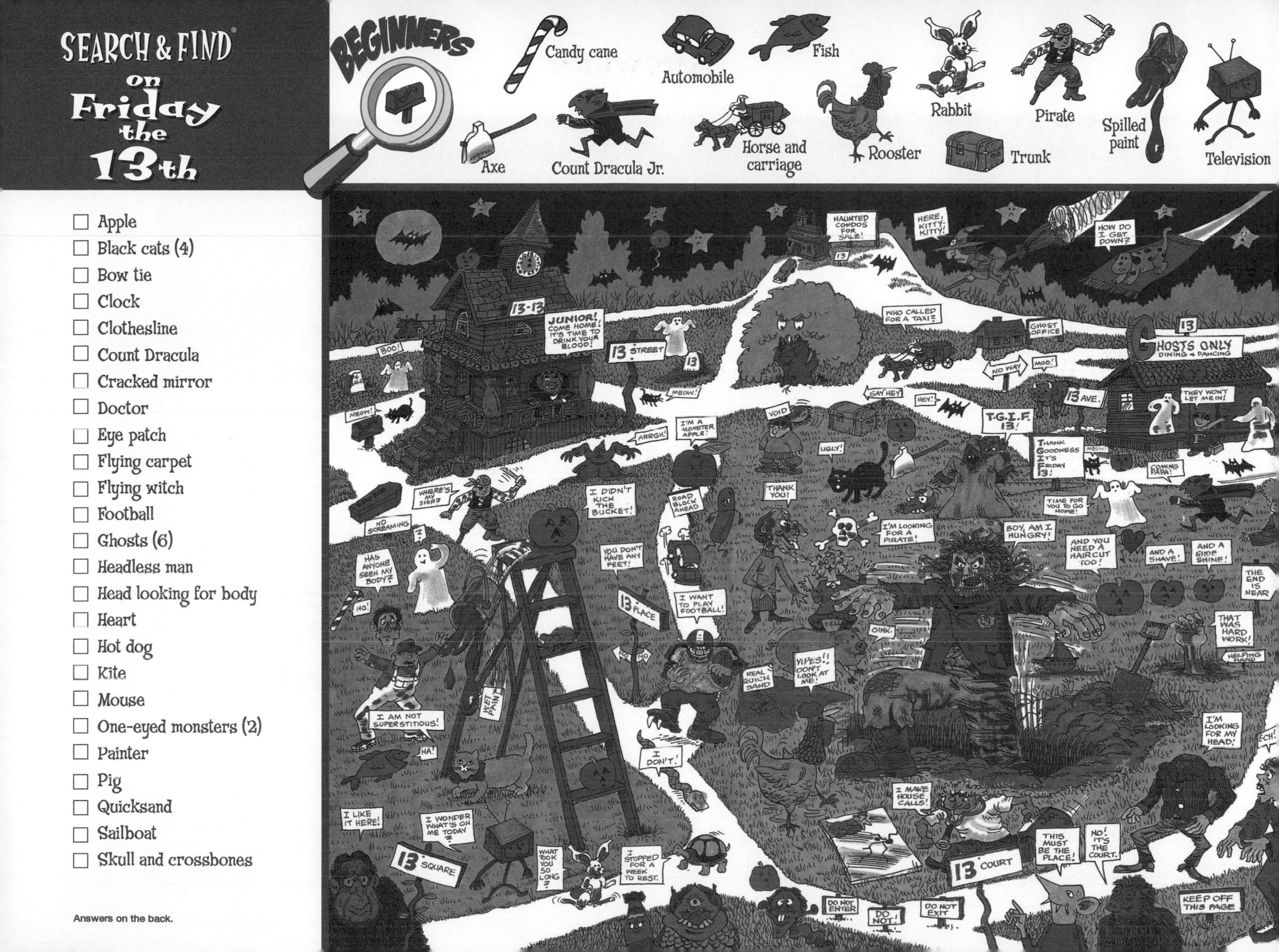
SEARCH & FIND®
on Friday the 13th
BEGINNERS
Candy cane
Automobile
Fish
Rabbit
Pirate
Spilled paint
Television
Axe
Count Dracula Jr.
Horse and carriage
Rooster
Trunk
☐ Apple
☐ Black cats (4)
☐ Bow tie
☐ Clock
☐ Clothesline
☐ Count Dracula
☐ Cracked mirror
☐ Doctor
☐ Eye patch
☐ Flying carpet
☐ Flying witch
☐ Football
☐ Ghosts (6)
☐ Headless man
☐ Head looking for body
☐ Heart
☐ Hot dog
☐ Kite
☐ Mouse
☐ One-eyed monsters (2)
☐ Painter
☐ Pig
☐ Quicksand
☐ Sailboat
☐ Skull and crossbones
Answers on the back.
HAUNTED CONDOS FOR SALE!
13
HERE, KITTY-KITTY!
HOW DO I GET DOWN?
13-13
JUNIOR! COME HOME! IT'S TIME TO DRINK YOUR BLOOD!
13 STREET
13
BOO!
MEOW!
MEOW!
WHO CALLED FOR A TAXI?
GHOST OFFICE
13
GHOSTS ONLY
DINING & DANCING
NO WAY
MOO!
13 AVE.
SAY HEY
HEY!
THEY WON'T LET ME IN!
VOID
I'M A MONSTER APPLE!
ARRGH!
T.G.I.F. 13!
THANK GOODNESS IT'S FRIDAY 13!
MEOW!
UGLY!
COMING PAPA!
WHERE'S MY SHIP?
I DIDN'T KICK THE BUCKET!
ROAD BLOCK AHEAD
THANK YOU!
TIME FOR YOU TO GO HOME!
NO SCREAMING
I'M LOOKING FOR A PIRATE!
BOY, AM I HUNGRY!
AND YOU NEED A HAIRCUT TOO!
AND A SHAVE!
AND A SHOE SHINE!
HAS ANYONE SEEN MY BODY?
YOU DON'T HAVE ANY FEET!
THE END IS NEAR
NO!
13 PLACE
I WANT TO PLAY FOOTBALL!
THAT WAS HARD WORK!
OINK.
HELPING HAND
NO
NO
REAL QUICK SAND
YIPES!! DON'T LOOK AT ME!
WET PAINT
I AM NOT SUPERSTITIOUS!
HA!
I DON'T.
I'M LOOKING FOR MY HEAD!
ECH!
I MAKE HOUSE CALLS!
I LIKE IT HERE!
I WONDER WHAT'S ON ME TODAY?
THIS MUST BE THE PLACE!
NO! IT'S THE COURT.
13 SQUARE
WHAT TOOK YOU SO LONG?
I STOPPED FOR A WEEK TO REST.
13 COURT
DO NOT ENTER
DO NOT!
DO NOT EXIT
KEEP OFF THIS PAGE

ANSWERS

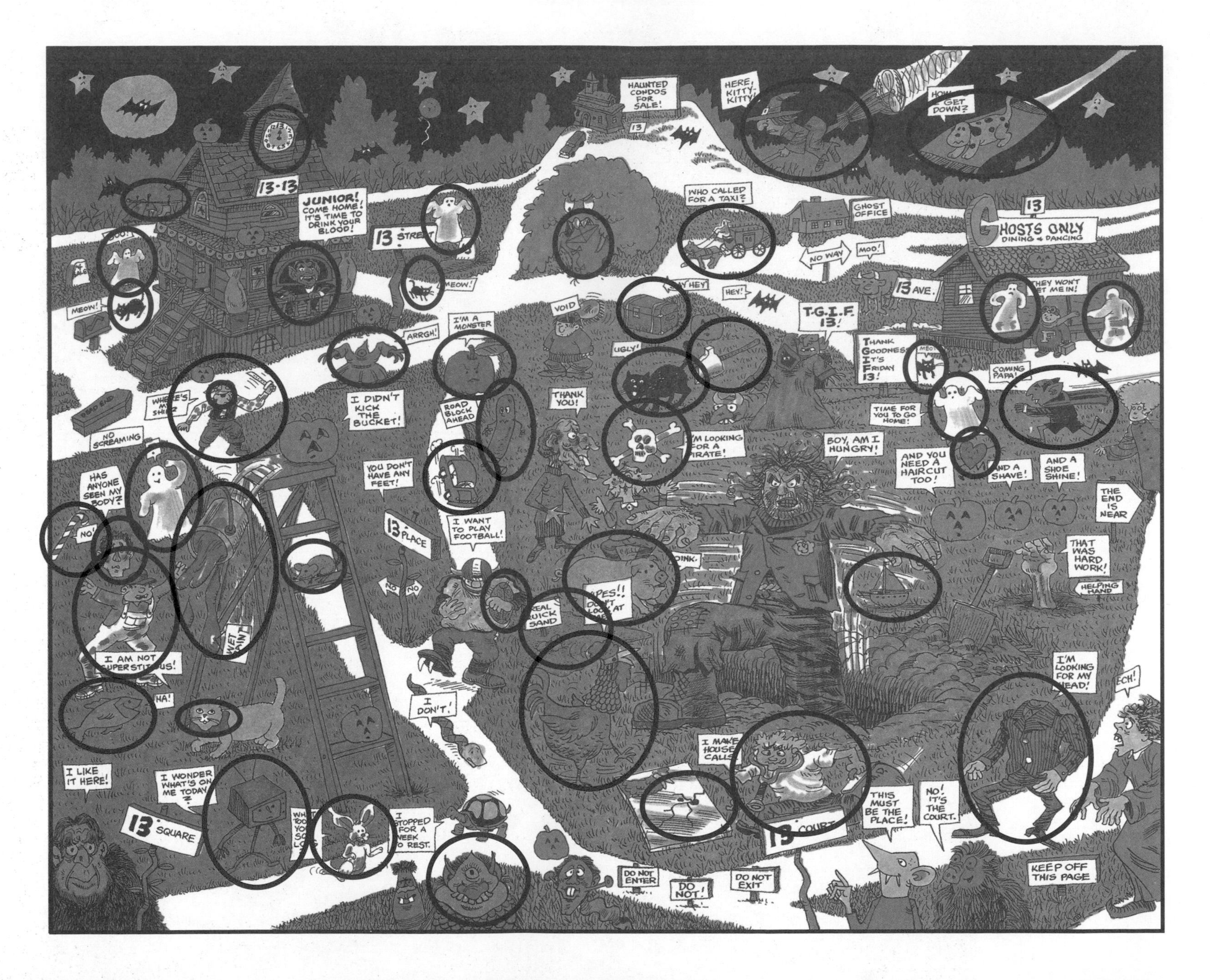

HAUNTED CONDOS FOR SALE!
13
HERE, KITTY, KITTY!
GET DOWN?
13-13
JUNIOR! COME HOME! IT'S TIME TO DRINK YOUR BLOOD!
BOO!
MEOW!
MEOW!
WHO CALLED FOR A TAXI?
GHOST OFFICE
NO WAY
MOO!
13
GHOSTS ONLY DINING & DANCING
13 AVE.
HEY!
HEY!
VOID
T-G-I-F 13!
THANK GOODNESS IT'S FRIDAY 13!
ARRGH!
I'M A MONSTER
UGLY!
COMING PAPA!
I DIDN'T KICK THE BUCKET!
ROAD BLOCK AHEAD
THANK YOU!
TIME FOR YOU TO GO HOME!
NO SCREAMING
BOY, AM I HUNGRY!
AND YOU NEED A HAIRCUT TOO!
AND A SHAVE!
AND A SHOE SHINE!
HAS ANYONE SEEN MY BODY?
YOU DON'T HAVE ANY FEET!
THE END IS NEAR
NO!
13 PLACE
I WANT TO PLAY FOOTBALL!
NO
NO
THAT WAS HARD WORK!
HELPING HAND
HA!
I'M LOOKING FOR MY HEAD!
I DON'T!
I LIKE IT HERE!
I WONDER WHAT'S ON ME TODAY?
13 SQUARE
I STOPPED FOR A WEEK TO REST.
THIS MUST BE THE PLACE!
NO! IT'S THE COURT.
DO NOT ENTER
DO NOT!
DO NOT EXIT
KEEP OFF THIS PAGE

SEARCH & FIND® at the Marathon

BEGINNERS

- Alien
- Astronaut
- Trombone
- Drummer
- Motorcycle
- Man in a barrel
- Surfer
- Skier
- Spotted dog
- Speed skater
- Octopus
- Count Dracula
- Strong man

- ☐ Angel
- ☐ Basketball
- ☐ Cane
- ☐ Chef
- ☐ Cowboy
- ☐ Deer
- ☐ Diving board
- ☐ Doctor
- ☐ Elephants (2)
- ☐ Firefighter
- ☐ Flying bats (5)
- ☐ Ice-cream cone
- ☐ Kite
- ☐ Moose's head
- ☐ Net
- ☐ Pail
- ☐ Periscope
- ☐ Police officer
- ☐ Rocket
- ☐ Roller skates
- ☐ Sad face
- ☐ Scooter
- ☐ Shortcut
- ☐ Snow White
- ☐ Sombrero
- ☐ Viking

Answers on the back.

ANSWERS

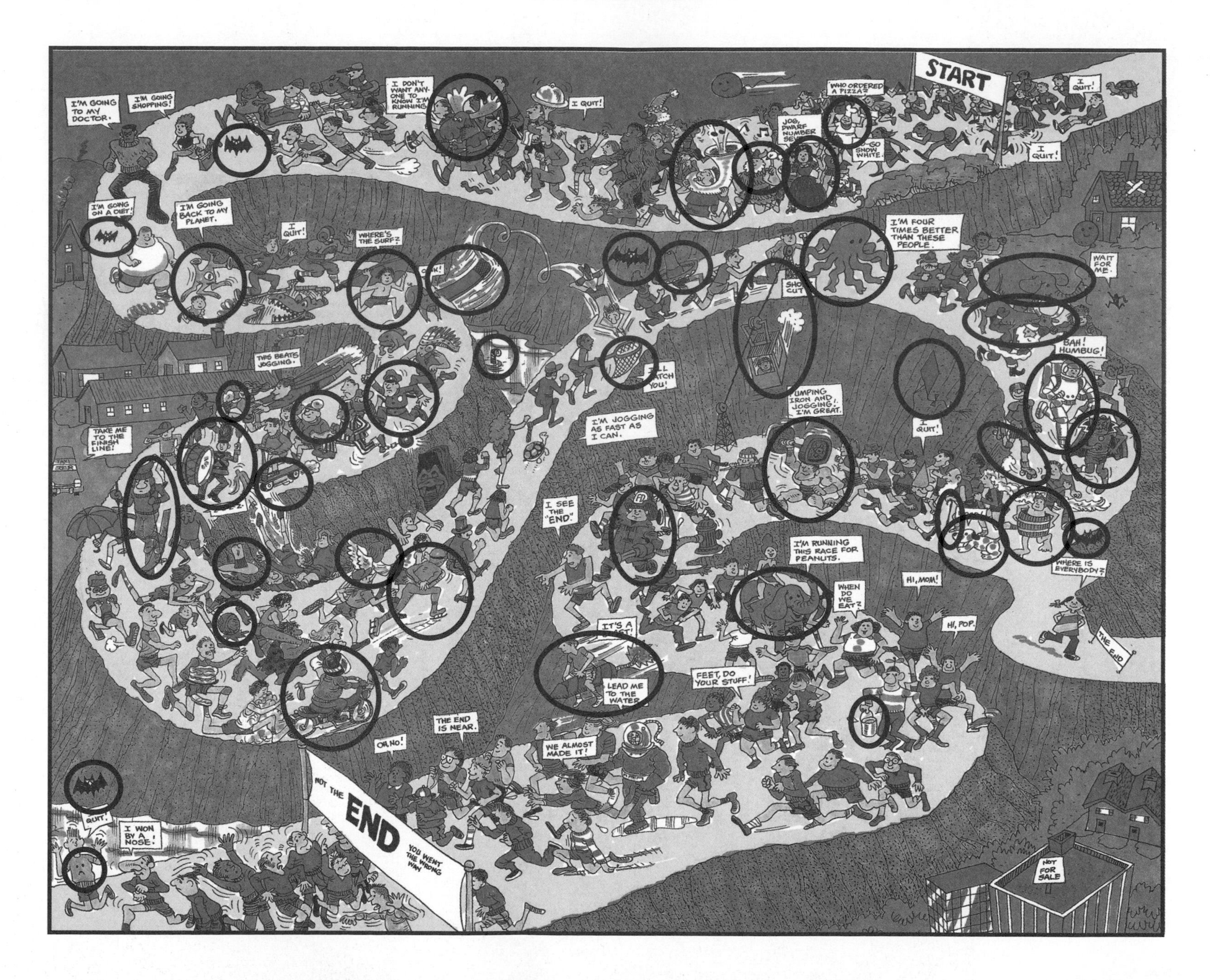

START
I'M GOING TO MY DOCTOR.
I'M GOING SHOPPING!
I DON'T WANT ANYONE TO KNOW I'M RUNNING.
I QUIT!
WHO ORDERED A PIZZA?
I QUIT!
I QUIT!
GO SHOW WHITE.
I'M GOING ON A DIET.
I'M GOING BACK TO MY PLANET.
I QUIT!
WHERE'S THE SURF?
I'M FOUR TIMES BETTER THAN THESE PEOPLE.
WAIT FOR ME.
TIPS BEATS JOGGING.
BAH! HUMBUG!
TAKE ME TO THE FINISH LINE!
I'M JOGGING AS FAST AS I CAN.
PUMPING IRON AND JOGGING. I'M GREAT.
I QUIT!
I SEE THE "END."
I'M RUNNING THIS RACE FOR PEANUTS.
WHERE IS EVERYBODY?
WHEN DO WE EAT?
HI, MOM!
HI, POP.
THE END
LEAD ME TO THE WATER
FEET, DO YOUR STUFF!
THE END IS NEAR.
OH, NO!
WE ALMOST MADE IT!
QUIT!
I WON BY A NOSE!
NOT THE END
YOU WENT THE WRONG WAY
NOT FOR SALE

SEARCH & FIND®

at the Super DogBowl

BEGINNERS

Ball

Cactus

Rooster

Ghost

Sign

Dog Aid cooler

Kicker

Bulldog

"Hop to it!"

Television

Number 4

Hobby horse

- ☐ "107"
- ☐ Bandaged tail
- ☐ Bench
- ☐ Binoculars
- ☐ Bowl of bones
- ☐ Candy cane
- ☐ Cracked egg
- ☐ Daisies (3)
- ☐ Dog pile
- ☐ Electrical outlet
- ☐ Heart-shaped turf
- ☐ Jack-o'-lanterns (5)
- ☐ "Last T.D."
- ☐ Manhole
- ☐ Mouse
- ☐ "No Ball Playing"
- ☐ Paint bucket
- ☐ Patched pants
- ☐ Pirate hat
- ☐ Pom-poms (2)
- ☐ Referees (2)
- ☐ Sleepy dogs (2)
- ☐ Star
- ☐ "Super Bowl I"
- ☐ Sword
- ☐ Target

Answers on the back.

ANSWERS

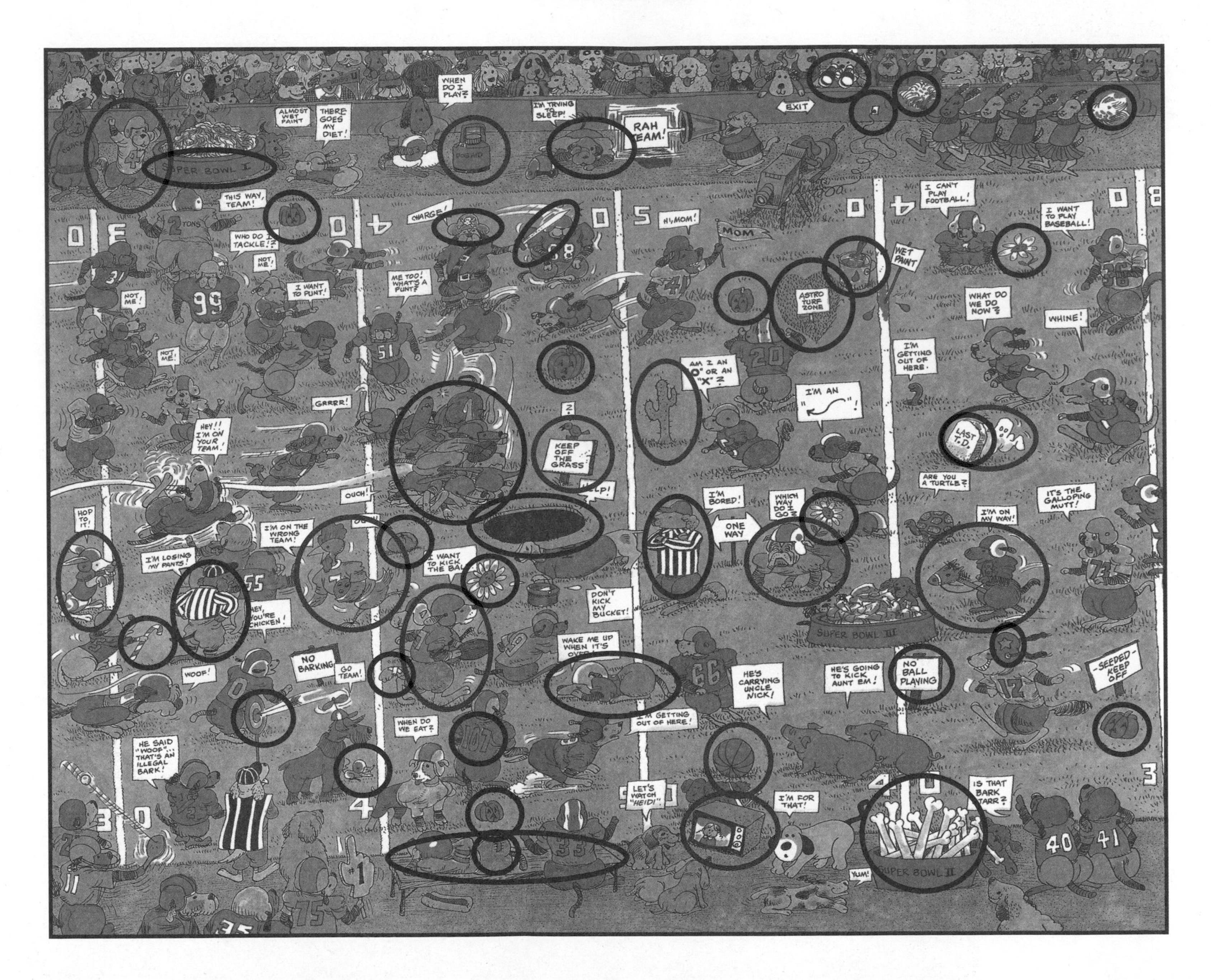
WHEN DO I PLAY?
ALMOST WET PAINT
THERE GOES MY DIET!
I'M TRYING TO SLEEP!
RAH TEAM!
EXIT
COACH
SUPER BOWL I
THIS WAY, TEAM!
TONS
CHARGE!
WHO DO I TACKLE!?
NOT ME!
I WANT TO PUNT!
ME TOO! WHAT'S A PUNT?
NOT ME!
NOT ME!
HI, MOM!
MOM
WET PAINT
ASTRO TURF ZONE
I CAN'T PLAY FOOTBALL!
I WANT TO PLAY BASEBALL!
WHAT DO WE DO NOW?
WHINE!
I'M GETTING OUT OF HERE.
AM I AN "O" OR AN "X"?
I'M AN "↶"!
LAST T.D.
GRRRR!
HEY!! I'M ON YOUR TEAM!
KEEP OFF THE GRASS
OUCH!
HOP TO IT!
I'M ON THE WRONG TEAM!
I'M LOSING MY PANTS!
HEY, YOU'RE CHICKEN!
DON'T KICK MY BUCKET!
I'M BORED!
ONE WAY
WHICH WAY DO I GO?
ARE YOU A TURTLE?
I'M ON MY WAY!
IT'S THE GALLOPING MUTT!
SUPER BOWL III
WOOF!
NO BARKING
GO TEAM!
WHEN DO WE EAT?
HE SAID "WOOF"... THAT'S AN ILLEGAL BARK!
I'M GETTING OUT OF HERE!
HE'S CARRYING UNCLE NICK!
HE'S GOING TO KICK AUNT EM!
NO BALL PLAYING
-SEEDED- KEEP OFF
LET'S WATCH "HEIDI".
I'M FOR THAT!
IS THAT BARK STARR?
YUM!
SUPER BOWL II

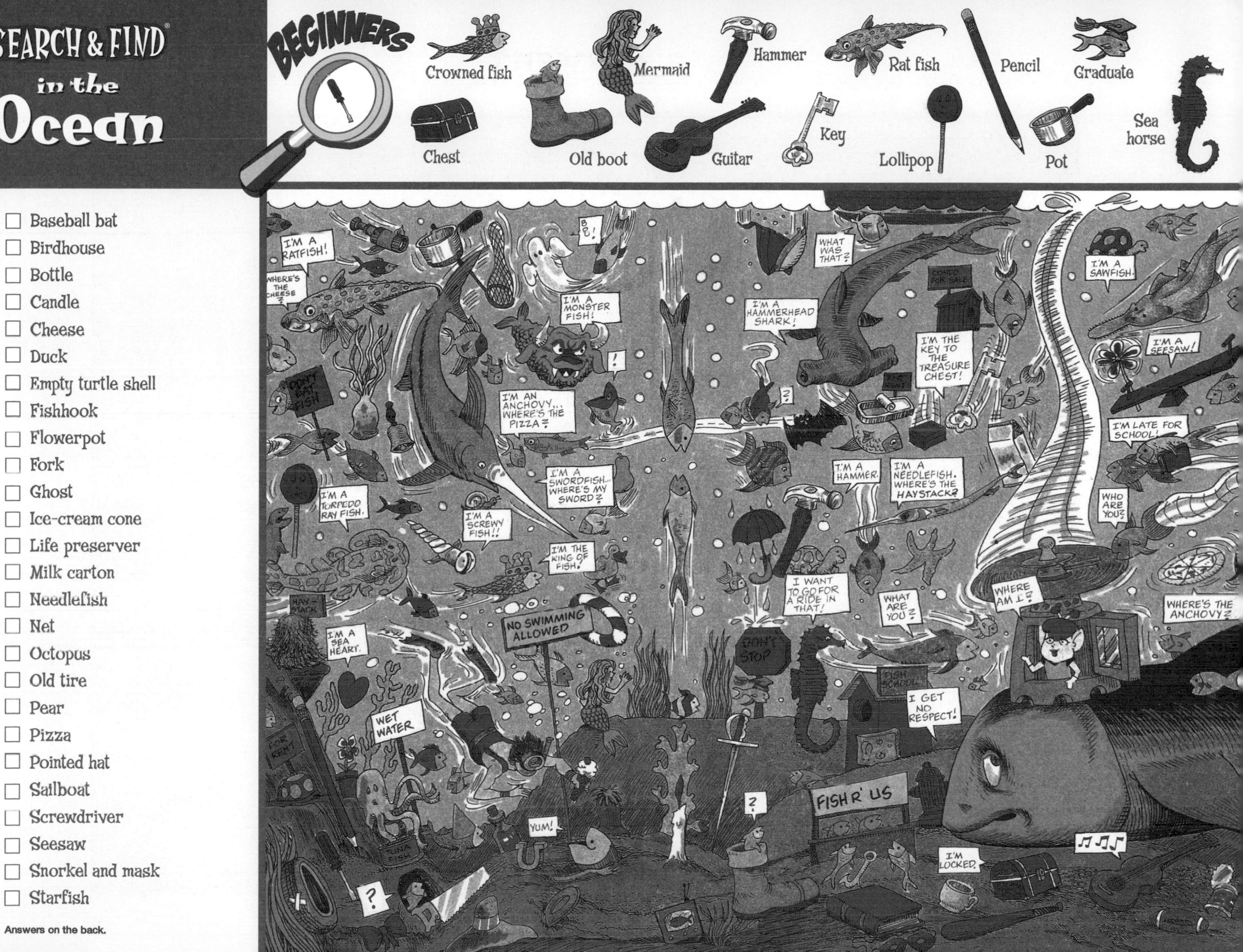

SEARCH & FIND®
in the
Ocean
BEGINNERS
Crowned fish
Mermaid
Hammer
Rat fish
Pencil
Graduate
Chest
Old boot
Guitar
Key
Lollipop
Pot
Sea horse
Baseball bat
Birdhouse
Bottle
Candle
Cheese
Duck
Empty turtle shell
Fishhook
Flowerpot
Fork
Ghost
Ice-cream cone
Life preserver
Milk carton
Needlefish
Net
Octopus
Old tire
Pear
Pizza
Pointed hat
Sailboat
Screwdriver
Seesaw
Snorkel and mask
Starfish
Answers on the back.
I'M A RATFISH!
WHERE'S THE CHEESE?
I'M A MONSTER FISH!
I'M AN ANCHOVY... WHERE'S THE PIZZA?
DON'T EAT FISH
I'M A SWORDFISH... WHERE'S MY SWORD?
I'M A TORPEDO RAY FISH.
I'M A SCREWY FISH!!
I'M THE KING OF FISH.
HAY-STACK
NO SWIMMING ALLOWED
I'M A SEA HEART.
WET WATER
FOR RENT
TUNA FISH
YUM!
WHAT WAS THAT?
I'M A HAMMERHEAD SHARK!
CONDO FOR SALE
I'M THE KEY TO THE TREASURE CHEST!
I'M A HAMMER.
I'M A NEEDLEFISH. WHERE'S THE HAYSTACK?
I WANT TO GO FOR A RIDE IN THAT!
DON'T STOP
WHAT ARE YOU?
FISH SCHOOL
I GET NO RESPECT!
FISH R' US
I'M LOCKED.
WHERE AM I?
I'M A SAWFISH.
I'M A SEESAW!
I'M LATE FOR SCHOOL!
WHO ARE YOU?
WHERE'S THE ANCHOVY?

ANSWERS

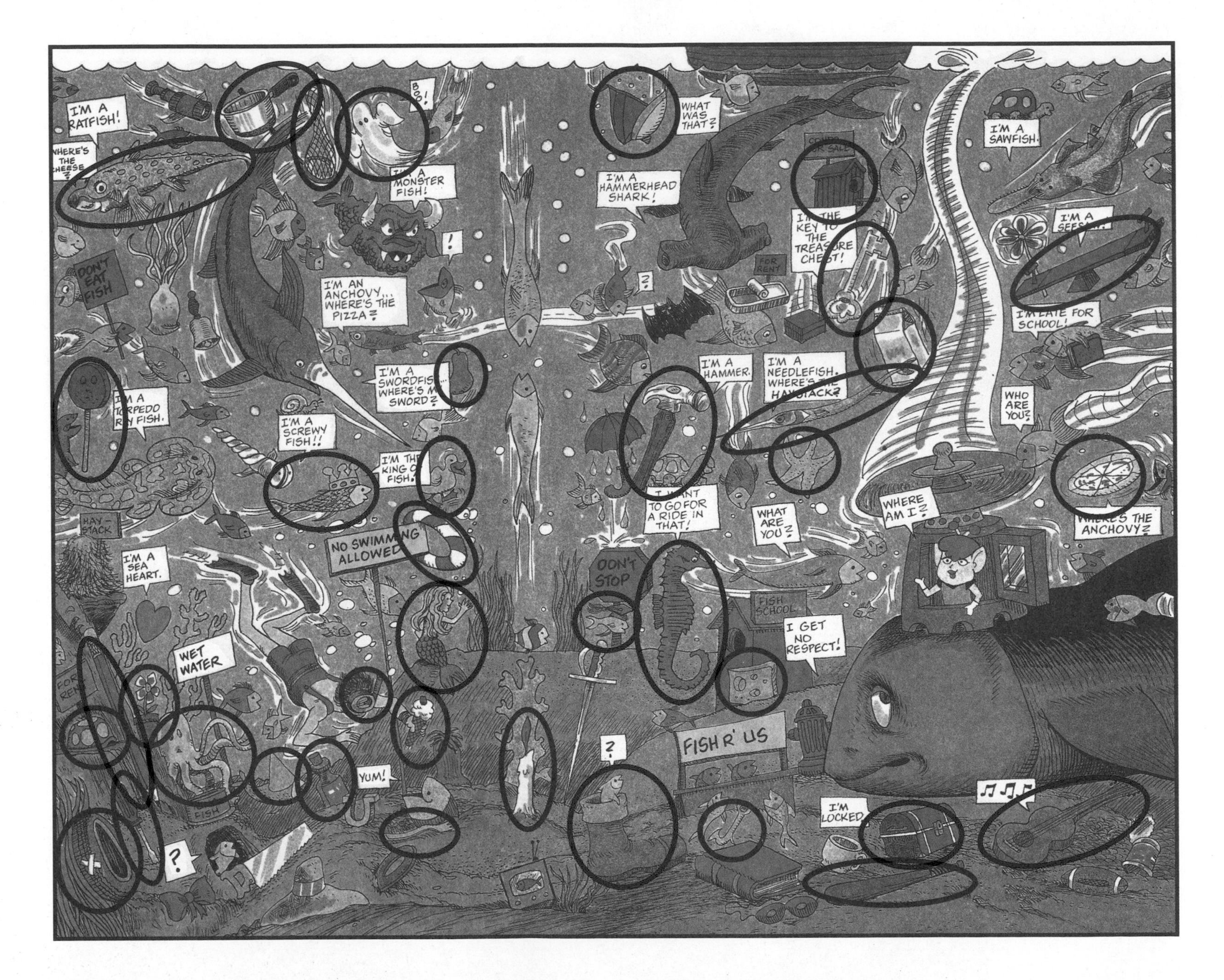

I'M A RATFISH!
DON'T EAT FISH
I'M AN ANCHOVY... WHERE'S THE PIZZA?
I'M A SCREWY FISH!!
I'M A HAMMERHEAD SHARK!
WHAT WAS THAT?
FOR RENT
I'M A SAWFISH.
I'M LATE FOR SCHOOL!
I'M A HAMMER.
WHO ARE YOU?
HAY-STACK
I'M A SEA HEART.
NO SWIMMING ALLOWED
WET WATER
YUM!
?
DON'T STOP
FISH SCHOOL
WHAT ARE YOU?
WHERE AM I?
I GET NO RESPECT!
FISH R' US
I'M LOCKED

SEARCH & FIND® at the Library

- ☐ Baseball
- ☐ Birdcage
- ☐ Bottle
- ☐ Bowling pins (10)
- ☐ Brooms (2)
- ☐ Cactus (2)
- ☐ Cake
- ☐ Candle
- ☐ Car
- ☐ Caveman
- ☐ Crown
- ☐ Frying pan
- ☐ Globe
- ☐ Hamburger
- ☐ Hearts (4)
- ☐ Hot dog
- ☐ Jack-in-the-box
- ☐ Monster hands (3)
- ☐ Music note
- ☐ Old tire
- ☐ Palm tree
- ☐ Pole-vaulter
- ☐ "Quiet" signs (7)
- ☐ Skulls (4)
- ☐ Smiley face

Answers on the back.

ANSWERS

DULL BOOKS
DRAMATIC BOOKS
CHILDREN'S BOOKS
WESTERN BOOKS
ROMANCE BOOKS
SEA BOOKS
NON BOOKS
QUIET
QUIET
QUIET
CHECK ROOM ▶
CASH ROOM
BIG BOOKS
WET FLOOR
OUCH!
SCI-FI BOOKS
HOW TO BOOKS
AUTO BOOKS
HUMOR BOOKS
TINY BOOKS
UNDER CONSTRUCTION
MONSTER BOOKS
FORE!
QUIET
MUSIC BOOKS
UP
QUIT
WESTERN BOOKS
SPORTS BOOKS
COOK BOOKS
QUIET
MYSTERY BOOKS
BEAM ME UP.
DETECTIVE BOOKS
QUIET
VIDEOS
THE UMPIRE STRIKES BACK
STAIR WARS
STAR WRECK
JAWZ
EXERCISE BOOKS
PENALTY-LATE BOOKS
LOST & FOUND
QUIET
WHERE ARE THE WESTERNS?
I WANT A DINO/KONG BOOK.
I'M LARRY.
A SPARE.
HISTORY BOOKS
WHERE'S THE LUNCH ROOM?
I'M LOOKING FOR A BOOK ON BREWS.

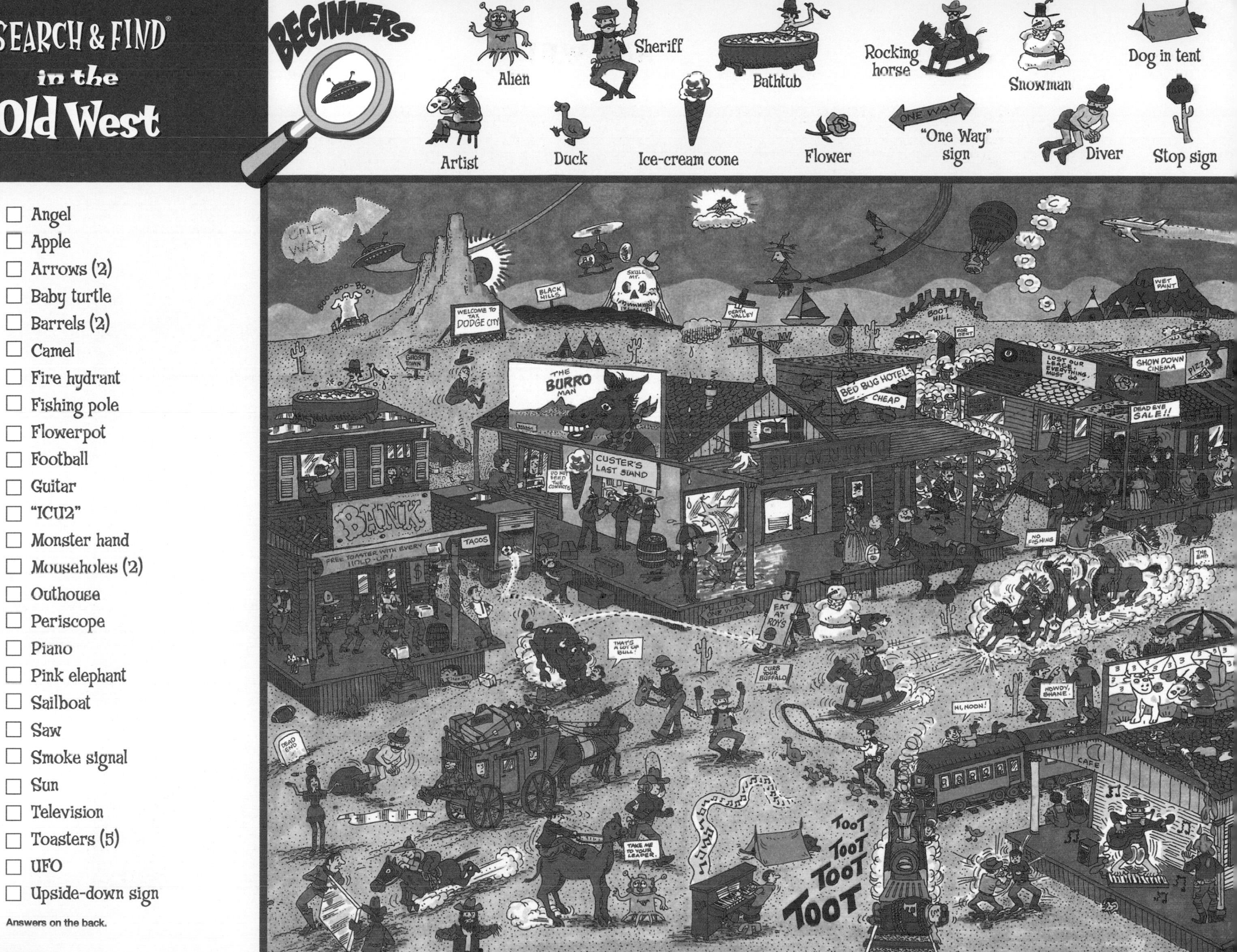

SEARCH & FIND®
in the
Old West
BEGINNERS
Artist
Alien
Duck
Sheriff
Ice-cream cone
Bathtub
Flower
Rocking horse
"One Way" sign
ONE WAY
Snowman
Diver
Dog in tent
Stop sign
Angel
Apple
Arrows (2)
Baby turtle
Barrels (2)
Camel
Fire hydrant
Fishing pole
Flowerpot
Football
Guitar
"ICU2"
Monster hand
Mouseholes (2)
Outhouse
Periscope
Piano
Pink elephant
Sailboat
Saw
Smoke signal
Sun
Television
Toasters (5)
UFO
Upside-down sign
Answers on the back.
ONE WAY
BOO-BOO-BOO!
WELCOME TO TAX DODGE CITY
BLACK HILLS
SKULL MT.
DEATH VALLEY
BOOT HILL
FOR RENT
WET PAINT
C O N D O S
GHOST TOWN
THE BURRO MAN
BED BUG HOTEL
CHEAP
LOST OUR LEASE EVERYTHING MUST GO
SHOW DOWN CINEMA
PIZZA
DEAD EYE SALE!!
CUSTER'S LAST STAND
DO NOT FEED THE CONVICTS
DO NOT READ THIS
BANK
FREE TOASTER WITH EVERY HOLD-UP!
TACOS
NO FISHING
THE END
ONE WAY
EAT AT ROY'S
THAT'S A LOT OF BULL!
CURB YOUR BUFFALO
HI, NOON!
HOWDY, SHANE.
DEAD END
CAFE
TAKE ME TO YOUR LEADER.
TOOT
TOOT
TOOT
TOOT

ANSWERS

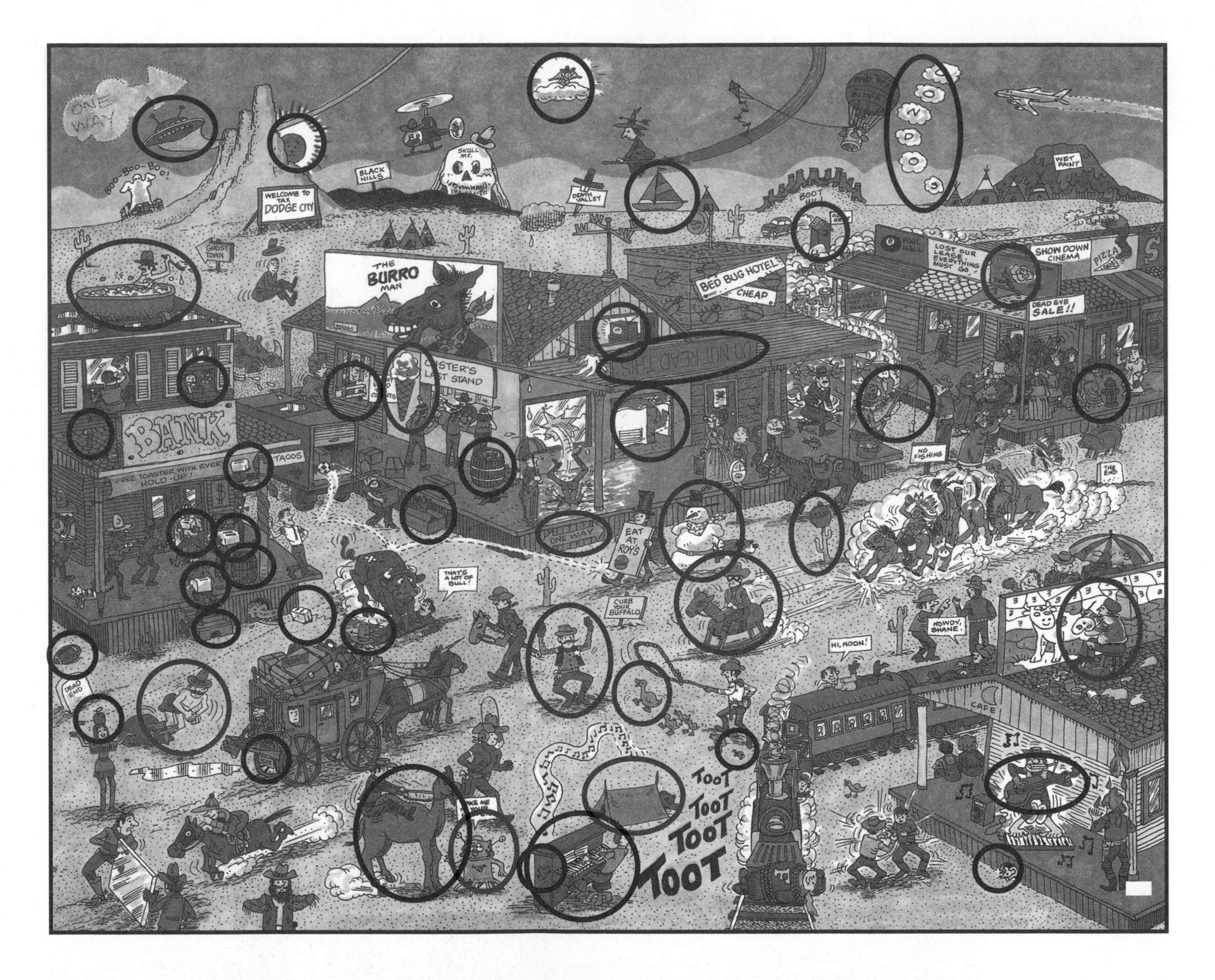
ONE WAY
BOO-BOO-BOO!
WELCOME TO TAX DODGE CITY
BLACK HILLS
SKULL MT.
DEATH VALLEY
WET PAINT
BOOT HILL
GHOST TOWN
THE BURRO MAN
BED BUG HOTEL
CHEAP
POOL HALL
LOST OUR LEASE EVERYTHING MUST GO
SHOW DOWN CINEMA
PIZZA
DEAD EYE SALE!!
CUSTER'S LAST STAND
DO NOT READ THIS
BANK
FREE TOASTER WITH EVERY HOLD-UP!
TACOS
NO FISHING
THE END
STOP
ONE WAY
EAT AT ROY'S
THAT'S A LOT OF BULL!
CURB YOUR BUFFALO
HOWDY, SHANE!
HI, NOON!
CAFE
DEAD END
TOOT
TOOT
TOOT
TOOT

SEARCH & FIND® among the Dog Catchers

- ☐ Bathing dog
- ☐ Briefcase
- ☐ Car antenna
- ☐ Cats (5)
- ☐ Convertible car
- ☐ "Dog Mail"
- ☐ Dollar signs (11)
- ☐ Empty bowls (2)
- ☐ Fire hose
- ☐ Fire hydrants (4)
- ☐ Fire truck
- ☐ Fishing pole
- ☐ Heart
- ☐ Howling dogs (2)
- ☐ Manhole
- ☐ Musical notes
- ☐ Net
- ☐ Piano
- ☐ Pink hats (7)
- ☐ Rope swing
- ☐ Satellite dish
- ☐ Sirens (2)
- ☐ Telephone truck
- ☐ Trash can
- ☐ "UDS"
- ☐ Umbrella

Answers on the back.

ANSWERS

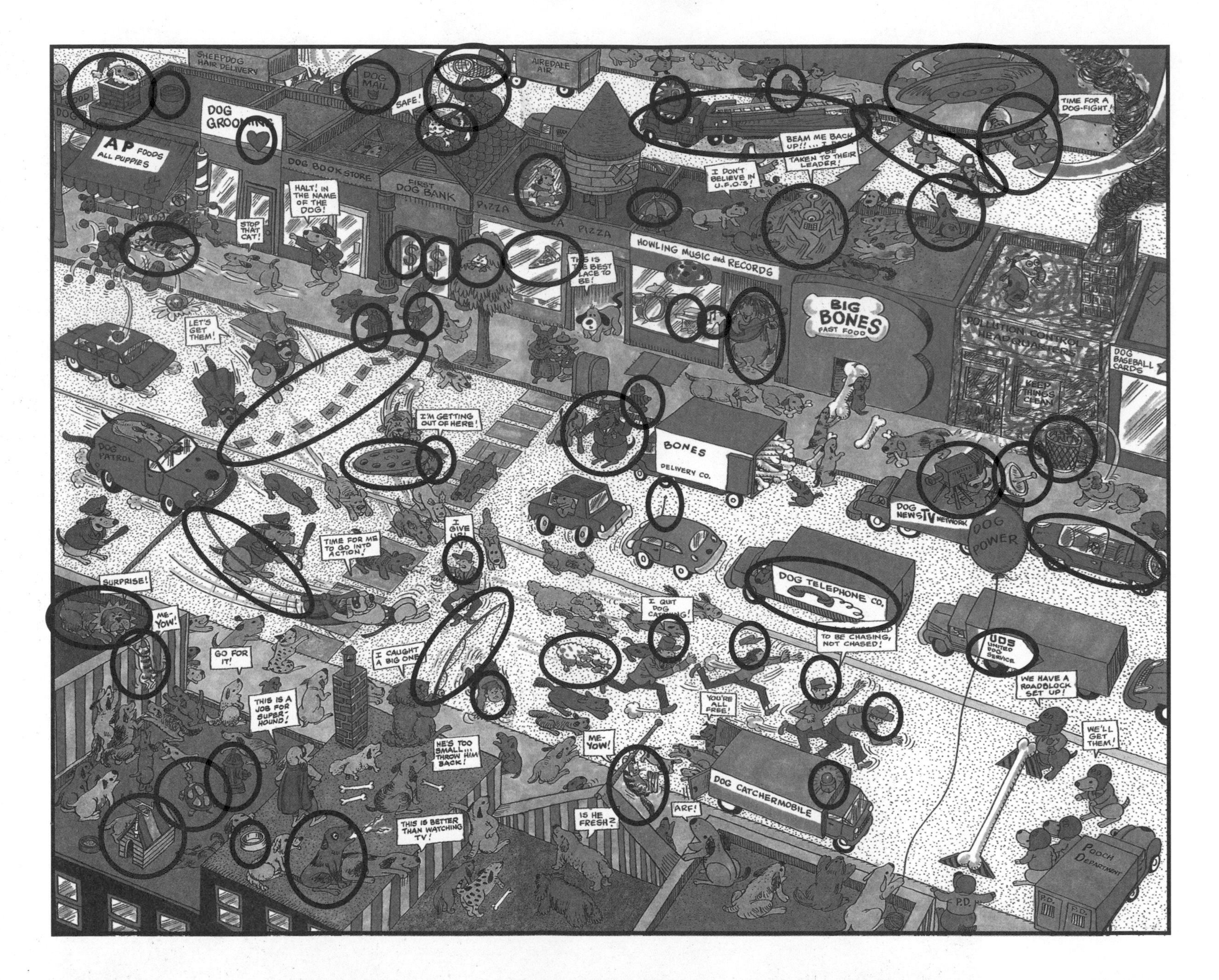
SHEEPDOG HAIR DELIVERY
AIREDALE AIR
DOG MAIL
SAFE!
AP FOODS ALL PUPPIES
DOG BOOK STORE
FIRST DOG BANK
HALT! IN THE NAME OF THE DOG!
STOP THAT CAT!
PIZZA
TIME FOR A DOG-FIGHT!
I DON'T BELIEVE IN U.F.O.'S!
HOWLING MUSIC and RECORDS
BIG BONES FAST FOOD
POLLUTION CONTROL HEADQUARTERS
DOG BASEBALL CARDS
KEEP THINGS CLEAN
LET'S GET THEM!
I'M GETTING OUT OF HERE!
DOG PATROL
BONES DELIVERY CO.
DOG NEWS TV NETWORK
DOG POWER
TIME FOR ME TO GO INTO ACTION!
DOG TELEPHONE CO.
SURPRISE!
ME-YOW!
GO FOR IT!
I CAUGHT A BIG ONE!
TO BE CHASING, NOT CHASED!
UDS UNITED DOG SERVICE
WE HAVE A ROADBLOCK SET UP!
WE'LL GET THEM!
THIS IS A JOB FOR SUPER-HOUND!
HE'S TOO SMALL... THROW HIM BACK!
ME-YOW!
YOU'RE ALL FREE!
IS HE FRESH?
ARF!
DOG CATCHERMOBILE
THIS IS BETTER THAN WATCHING TV!
POOCH DEPARTMENT
P.D.

SEARCH & FIND®
at a
TV Quiz
Show
BEGINNERS
Dog collar
Hot-dog seller
Fairy
Flashlight
Pink dog
Sock
"HOWL" sign
Director
Candle
Pearl necklace
Steak
Dog in sweater
Fire hydrant
Announcer
"Arf TV" (3)
Boxes (3)
Camera
Chef
Clipboard
Clothespins (2)
Contestants (4)
Crown
Dog food
Drum
Elephant
"Exit"
Flowerpot
Game wheel
Giraffe
Gold bar
Gorilla
Headphones (6)
Magic wand
Oilcan
Party hat
Pencil
Pile of bones
"Prizes"
Space dog
Answers on the back.
V.I.P. ROOM (VERY IMPORTANT PUPS)
HI, POP!
SHOULD I END THIS?
LET'S GO DOGS!
QUIET
THE ANSWER IS "DOGFIGHT"!
EXIT
DO YOU COME HERE OFTEN?
NOT IF I CAN HELP IT!
WHERE'S TARZAN?
THRILLING!
WOOF!
I'M HUNGRY!
HI, MOM!
I CAN'T SEE!
YOU'RE LUCKY!
I'M WATCHING WRESTLING.
Z-Z-Z-Z!
ARF TV
D G F G T
DOG BOWL TV GAME
BLANK!
IT'S STILL GOING ON!
THERE ARE 2 G'S!
HE MUST BE THE BIG CHEESE!
IS IT OVER YET?
I'M AN APPRENTICE.
I HOPE NO ONE SEES ME HERE!
TAKE 1
ARF-ARF!
DULL!
VERY!
AM I ON CAMERA?
BOW-WOW-WOW!
HOWL
GO...GO GO!
HELLO
I WISH I COULD!
IS THIS A REPEAT?
IT SHOULD BE.
UGH!
OUT OF SIGHT!
HOORAY FOR VANNA BARK!
I WISH IT WAS.
PRIZE$
GOLD
GRRR-REAT!
I WANT TO GO HOME!
I LIKE THE PRIZES.
I LIKE THE COMMERCIALS

ANSWERS

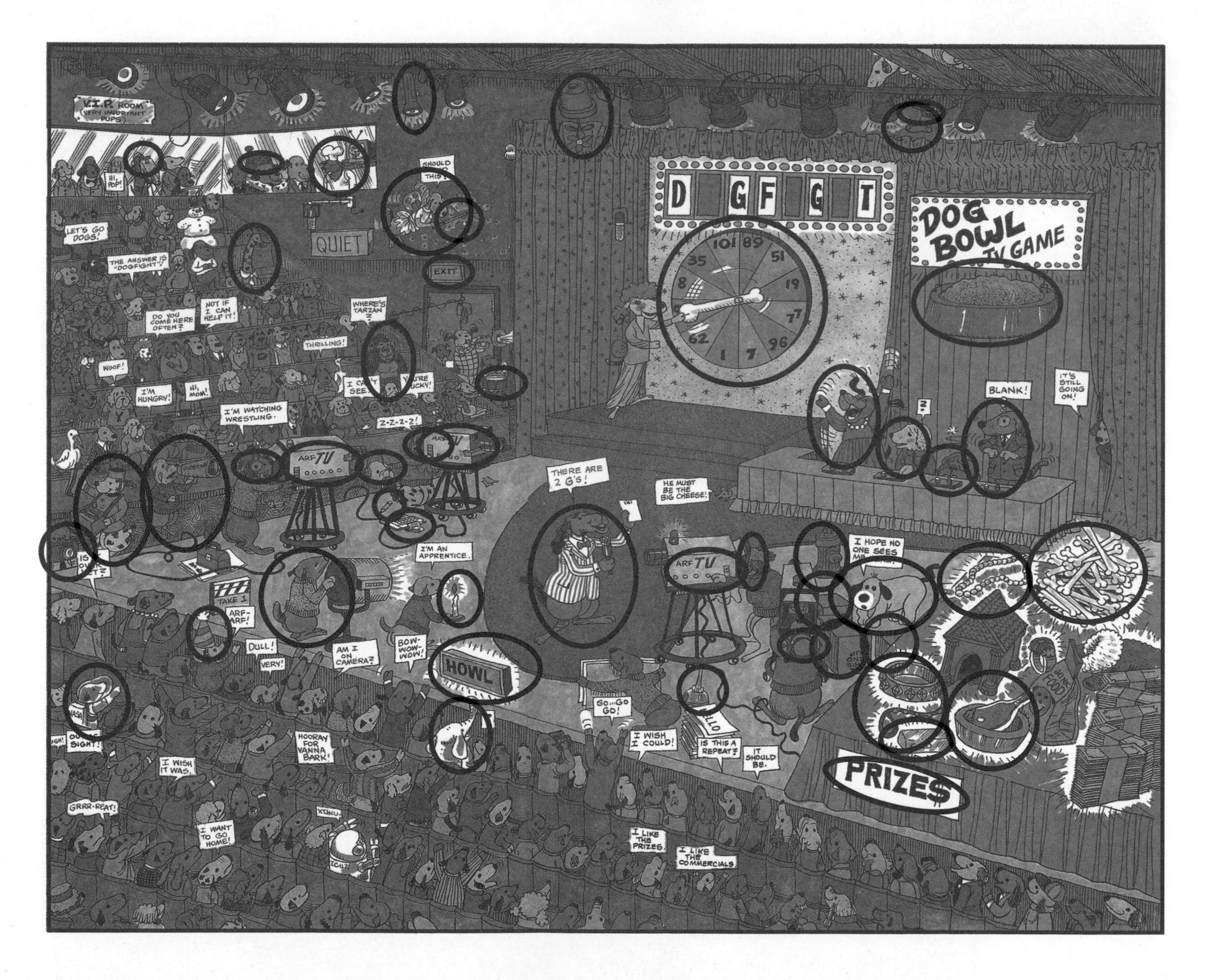
V.I.P. ROOM
(VERY IMPORTANT PUPS)
HI, POP!
LET'S GO DOGS!
THE ANSWER IS "DOGFIGHT"
QUIET
EXIT
DO YOU COME HERE OFTEN?
NOT IF I CAN HELP IT!
WHERE'S TARZAN?
THRILLING!
WOOF!
I'M HUNGRY!
HI, MOM!
I'M WATCHING WRESTLING.
Z-Z-Z-Z!
ARF TV
D G F G T
DOG BOWL TV GAME
101 89 51 19 77 96 7 1 62 8 35
BLANK!
IT'S STILL GOING ON!
THERE ARE 2 G'S!
HE MUST BE THE BIG CHEESE!
I'M AN APPRENTICE.
TAKE 1
ARF-ARF!
DULL!
VERY!
AM I ON CAMERA?
BOW-WOW-WOW!
HOWL
GO...GO GO!
I WISH I COULD!
IS THIS A REPEAT?
IT SHOULD BE.
JUNK FOOD
PRIZE$
HOORAY FOR VANNA BARK!
I WISH IT WAS.
GRRR-REAT!
I WANT TO GO HOME!
I LIKE THE PRIZES.
I LIKE THE COMMERCIALS

SEARCH & FIND® at a Rock Concert

- [ ] Alien
- [ ] Ape
- [ ] Artist
- [ ] Barbell
- [ ] Bouquet of flowers
- [ ] Bowling ball
- [ ] Clown
- [ ] Doctor
- [ ] Drummer
- [ ] Fish tank
- [ ] Flamingo
- [ ] Ghosts (4)
- [ ] Guitars (4)
- [ ] Hot-dog stand
- [ ] Knight
- [ ] Lamppost
- [ ] Masked man
- [ ] Mummy
- [ ] Prisoner
- [ ] Rabbit
- [ ] Skateboard
- [ ] Snowman
- [ ] Stars (6)
- [ ] Tin Man
- [ ] Tombstones (2)
- [ ] Worm

Answers on the back.

ANSWERS

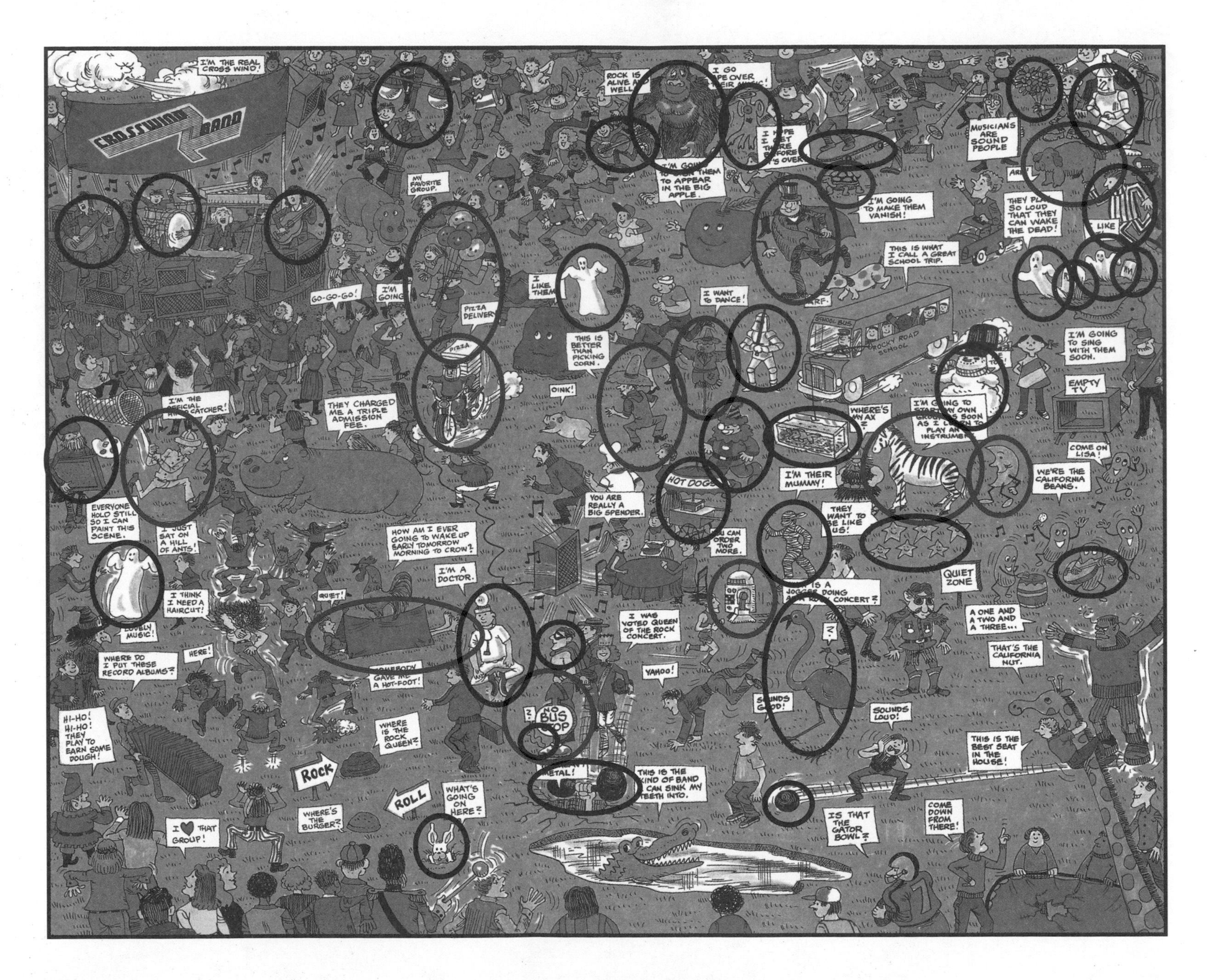

I'M THE REAL CROSS WIND!
CROSSWIND BAND
MY FAVORITE GROUP.
I'M GOING TO MAKE THEM VANISH!
MUSICIANS ARE SOUND PEOPLE
THIS IS WHAT I CALL A GREAT SCHOOL TRIP.
GO-GO-GO!
I'M GOING
PIZZA DELIVERY
I WANT TO DANCE!
SCHOOL BUS
ROCKY ROAD SCHOOL
THIS IS BETTER THAN PICKING CORN.
I'M GOING TO SING WITH THEM SOON.
EMPTY TV
OINK!
THEY CHARGED ME A TRIPLE ADMISSION FEE.
COME ON LISA!
WE'RE THE CALIFORNIA BEANS.
I'M THEIR MUMMY!
HOT DOGS
YOU ARE REALLY A BIG SPENDER.
EVERYONE HOLD STILL SO I CAN PAINT THIS SCENE.
I JUST SAT ON A HILL OF ANTS!
HOW AM I EVER GOING TO WAKE UP EARLY TOMORROW MORNING TO CROW?
I'M A DOCTOR.
QUIET ZONE
A ONE AND A TWO AND A THREE...
I THINK I NEED A HAIRCUT!
QUIET!
I WAS VOTED QUEEN OF THE ROCK CONCERT.
THAT'S THE CALIFORNIA NUT.
WHERE DO I PUT THESE RECORD ALBUMS?
HERE!
YAHOO!
SOUNDS LOUD!
HI-HO! HI-HO! THEY PLAY TO EARN SOME DOUGH!
WHERE IS THE ROCK QUEEN?
THIS IS THE BEST SEAT IN THE HOUSE!
ROCK
ROLL
THIS IS THE KIND OF BAND I CAN SINK MY TEETH INTO.
WHAT'S GOING ON HERE?
WHERE'S THE BURGER?
I ♥ THAT GROUP!
IS THAT THE GATOR BOWL?
COME DOWN FROM THERE!